BIDSTON OBSERVATORY

The Place and the People

Joyce Scoffield

*Best wishes,
Joyce Scoffield*

Countyvise Ltd

The watercolour painting on the cover is by Sylvia Asquith,
for many years a member of the Observatory staff.

First Published 2006 by Countyvise Limited,
14 Appin Road, Birkenhead, Wirral CH41 9HH.

The right of Joyce Scoffield to be identified as the author of this work has been asserted by
her in accordance with the Copyright, Design and Patents Act 1988.

British Library Cataloguing in Publication Data.
A catalogue record for this book is available from the British Library.

Please note: From 1st January 2007 ISBNs will contain 13 numbers these numbers will be
the same as the present number printed below the barcode (ie. starting 978).
Countyvise is showing both existing (10 digit) and future (13 digit) ISBNs on the Title page
verso. Please continue to use the 10 figure number until 31st December 2006.

ISBN 1 901231 68 2   ISBN 978 1 901231 68 7

Acknowledgements

My thanks go to the following people:

Marianne Elliott - Assistant Curator of Physical Sciences at
the World Museum - for her patient assistance over many
months.
Professor Peter Davies - Emeritus Professor of History at
the University of Liverpool, for reading the manuscript and
suggesting appropriate amendments.
The Friends of the University of Liverpool, for their
generous financial support.
Adrian Allan - the Archivist of the University of Liverpool.
Liverpool World Museum Archive Department
Merseyside Maritime Museum
Wirral Museum
Cheshire Record Office
Liverpool Central Library
Birkenhead Central Library
Greasby Library
The Sydney Jones Library (University of Liverpool)
The Harold Cohen Library (University of Liverpool)
Williamson Art Gallery
P.D.Hingley - Librarian at the Royal Astronomical Society
Professor Mark Bailey of Armagh Observatory

Staff of the Proudman Oceanographic Laboratory:
Professor John Huthnance
Professor Philip Woodworth
Dr. Eric Jones
Colin Bell
Julia Martin
Linda Parry
John Mackinnon
Robert Smith
Libby MacLeod

Former Staff of the Proudman Oceanographic Laboratory:
Dr. Brian McCartney
Joan Rossiter
Valerie Doodson MBE and the late Thomas Doodson
Professor Geoffrey Lennon
Sylvia Asquith
Eunice Murrell
Meryl Eilbeck
Alex Kerr

Other information or material was provided by:
Audrey Corkan
Mary Connell
Stan Davies
Stan Amos
Ronald Brown
Glyn Holden
Mr J C Evans
Geoff. Bratt
Gerard Gilligan of the Liverpool Astronomical Society
The late Donald Whiteside

Above all my thanks go to my husband, Alan, for his
unstinting help, advice and patience.

CONTENTS

PART II - SOME INDIVIDUAL ASPECTS

Introduction

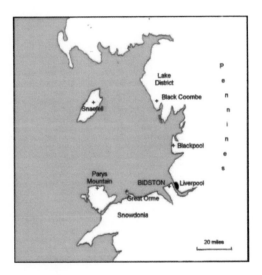

Bidston Observatory stands on the seaward end of a ridge of fairly high land which is parallel with the River Mersey and is opposite Liverpool.

To the east we have a panoramic view over the City of Liverpool, with the Pennines forming a backdrop on clear days.

Northwards we look over Liverpool Bay to Blackpool Tower, and quite often Black Coombe and the hills of the southern Lake District are visible.

To the west, across the Dee Estuary, we can see the Great Orme at Llandudno, and on a clear day the mountains of Snowdonia can also be seen in the background. On exceptionally clear occasions Parys Mountain on Anglesey becomes just visible, but sightings are uncommon. In thirty years of meteorological observation I have seen Anglesey on only a handful of occasions.

If one is permitted to climb to the highest accessible point above the Observatory roof, and one looks out to the northwest in late afternoon on a day of really exceptional visibility, the tip of Snaefell Mountain on the Isle of Man can be seen. I have never had that good fortune, but one or two of my colleagues have done so. The last officially recorded sighting was in 1956.

Just as such an extensive area is visible from Bidston, so Bidston has been a prominent landmark for shipping approaching the Mersey for several centuries, and its windmill and banqueting house appear as leading marks on charts as far back as 1693.

To set the stage for the building of the Observatory it is desirable to consider the history of the hill.

It was part of the manor of Bidston, which in 1397 was bought by Sir John Stanley, Knight, who was the great-grandfather of the first Earl of Derby. In 1408 permission was granted to "empark with palings, wall, ditch or hedge 80 acres of the demesne adjacent to their manor of Bidston." The wall which was built would appear to be the "Penny-a-Day Dyke", so-called because of a local tradition that its builders were paid that amount for their work. There is a reference to the old park wall in 1609, and parts of the wall still stand along the western edge of the hill-top (see photo below). Thus the top of the hill was outside the deer park and came to be regarded as common land. It was, however, part of the estate until 1893, when it became public property.

W.G.Herdman, the artist, writing in 1898, commented that:

"For many years Bidston Hill was a general resort of picnic parties and pleasure seekers. During the first half of this century (the nineteenth) it was entirely open to the public and was only enclosed by the proprietor, Mr. Vyner, when the visitors began to abuse the privileges accorded them."[1]

The photo shows the path leading down towards Bidston Village. Surviving parts of the old deer park wall are on the left, and the boundary wall of the Observatory and lighthouse is on the right.

Sir John Stanley also obtained a licence to embattle his castle of Liverpool and evidently travelled fairly often between there and Bidston. In 1414 he was attacked by Sir Henry Norris' men, who stole the boat in which he crossed the Mersey to his recently acquired manor of Bidston. This was the first record of a link between Liverpool and Bidston, a link which underlies much of the subject matter of this book.

The Bidston estate belonged to the Stanley family for 250 years, until the time of the Commonwealth. The seventh Earl of Derby was beheaded for his support of King Charles I and the Earl's widow and son found it necessary to sell the estate in 1653. It passed through the hands of a Councellor Steele (Recorder of London) and Lord Kingston. In1680 it became subject to negotiations by Sir Robert Vyner, a goldsmith and banker of London, whose nephew completed the purchase some years later, and whose family owned the estate until the Twentieth Century.

This, then, is the background to the story of the connections between Liverpool, the sea and Bidston.

Chapter One

The Flag System

The introduction of the flag system at Bidston may have been prompted by the end of the Seven Years War 1756 - 1763, for, on May 11th 1763, the Liverpool Council ordered that "A Signal House for Shipping be built on the Rock Land in Cheshire at the expense of the Dock Duties according to the Plan now laid before the Council by Mr. Lightoller, and that Robert Gwillym Esq. be admitted to fit up and have such Rooms therein as he shall think proper during the pleasure of the Council, not prejudicing the said Building nor the use thereof ...."[1]

Before this time vessels approaching Liverpool from the Irish Sea had no way of notifying their owners of their imminent arrival. Most Liverpool-bound ships sailed into the Hoyle Lake just off the most westerly point of Wirral and proceeded in a NE direction along the coast using the Rock Channel. Thus the ships could not be observed from Liverpool because the land mass of the Wirral Peninsula obscured them until they turned into the River Mersey off the point now known as New Brighton, and they were close to the Liverpool waterfront before they could be identified. As a consequence the shipowners had very little time to make preparation for the offloading of their cargoes. It was realised that, because of the panoramic views from Bidston Hill on the Wirral, a lookout placed there could see the vessels whilst they were still several hours' or even days' sailing time from port. With the aid of a powerful telescope he would be able to identify the house-flag flying at the masthead. The shipowner waiting in Liverpool, knowing that one of his ships was due, could, for his part, clearly see Bidston Hill, for in those days there were few trees or tall buildings to block his view.

Land was leased from Mr. Vyner, a system of flags was devised, and a signal house or tower was set up on Bidston Hill, not far from the site of the present lighthouse. A line of flagpoles was erected, extending from the tower southwards along the hill towards the windmill (see enclosure inside back cover)[2]. Each flagpole carried the flag of a particular shipowner. In that way the owners would know whereabouts on the hill to look for their personal signal. Mr. Vyner charged each merchant a nominal five shillings per annum for the privilege of erecting a flagpole.[3] In the early stages there was one flagpole per shipping company, but as time went on the number of shipowners increased, so more flagpoles were erected, some of them reaching as far as, then beyond, the windmill while others were located further on than the lookout tower in a northerly direction. Before long the number of shipping companies involved exceeded the number of flagpoles available, and eventually each flagpole was required to carry up to three flags at any one time.

As a vessel came within sight of Bidston, its master ordered the signal flag of the shipowner to be hoisted. The lookout at

Bidston identified the signal, picked out the appropriate flag from the stock in his hut, and hurried out onto the hill to the appropriate flagstaff to raise the flag. This was recognised by a member of the shipowner's staff watching from one of the elevated sites in Liverpool, such as Everton Heights. He, in turn, notified the owner, thus giving him plenty of time to prepare for docking and unloading.

According to Picton, the churchyard of St. Nicholas Church close to the waterfront, and the adjoining coffee house, were the best places for viewing the signal flags.[4]

The earliest reference I have found to the flag system comes from "History of Liverpool", variously attributed to J. Wallace - 1795 or to Dr. W. Moss - 1801. The author states that there were 58 flagstaffs erected near the lighthouse (see Chapter Two) on Bidston Hill. Of these, 49 carried the flags of particular merchants, the rest were "to shew if the vessels coming in are Greenlanders, men of war, or if the vessel is ship, brig or snow ; there are also immediate signals to the town of all vessels seen in distress in either of the channels" (i.e. the Rock Channel and the Formby Channel) "that thereby speedy assistance may be given. The method used to convey intelligence to the town, so as to inform every merchant of the arrival of his ship, is for the masters of the several vessels, as soon as they make the light-house, to hoist a particular signal, which is previously agreed, to denote the respective merchant to whom the ship belongs; this being seen from the signal-house, instantly directs what flag to hoist for the information of the merchant on shore; these signals on a clear day may be seen from St. Domingo, Everton, St. James's

Walk, etc., by the naked eye as far as the N.W. buoy, and in hazy weather easily distinguished by good glasses from thence, or from any of the lower parts of the town. This is a most eligible and commendable plan, and of greater utility than that of Maker Tower at Plymouth, which is partial in its signals, whereas this being general, is what no other part of the kingdom can claim."[5]

At Bidston there were three flagstaffs mounted on the roof of the lookout tower for the purpose of identifying the type of vessel approaching the port. The flagstaff at the northern end was used to signal the approach of a ketch or hey, the middle one a brig or snow, and the southern one a ship. There was an oblique pole on the north side of the building, to signal any problems experienced by a vessel sailing in from the west via the Rock or Hoyle Channel, and a second oblique pole on the south side for problems experienced by vessels coming in via the Formby Channel.

These signals (presumably used by the ships' captains and by the Bidston lookout) were:-
Ship in distress :- Ball + flag at half-mast.[6]
Brig or small vessel in distress :- Cone upright + flag at half-mast
Snow in distress :- Cone up-ended + flag at half-mast
If vessels experienced distress when outward bound, broad pendants were displayed instead of flags.

In his poem 'The Sailor', written about 1805, Edward Anderson, for many years master of the Brig "Jemina", says:
A flag is hoisted on the Bidston Hill,

A signal for a ship that's homeward bound -
She proves a prize with twenty thousand pound;
The bells they ring, the ship she comes in sight,
And crowds of people view her with delight.[7]

Albert Smith, in his book "The Struggles and Adventures of Christopher Tadpole at Home and Abroad" published in 1847-48, described how a young boy, rescued from the Cheshire salt-mines around the turn of the century, was being led over Bidston Hill by his rescuer, the showman Hickory, to the Ring O'Bells Inn in Bidston Village. The boy saw the lights of Liverpool and took them to be those of a large salt-mine. The sight was so riveting to the boy that, to quote Albert Smith, "he could not take his eyes from it, scarcely even to notice the lighthouse under whose very walls they passed, with its array of signal masts that looked as if somebody was either preparing a great display of fireworks, or making ready to set sail, and carry the entire hill, lighthouse, telegraph, and all, out to sea, upon the first fair wind."[8]

Liverpool pottery manufacture peaked around the end of the 18th Century, and anything connected with shipping and the sea was popular for the decoration of earthenware jugs and pots. The signal station on Bidston Hill was a favourite subject, and a fine display of pottery depicting the flag masts can be seen in the Merseyside Maritime Museum (see photo - courtesy National Museums Liverpool).[9]

The mug depicted below, dated 1788, shows a row of 44 flags, together with a list of the appropriate shipowners. There is, in the centre of the row, a drawing of the tower on Bidston Hill showing its three signal masts. On the right of the drawing is the octagonal lighthouse built in 1772.[10]

Courtesy National Museums Liverpool

As time progressed the number of flags and ship-owners' names shown on pottery increased steadily. More than 75 poles were depicted on the pottery produced by the Herculaneum Factory in the first quarter of the 19th century.

A map of the County Palatine of Chester, drawn up from actual surveys made by A. Bryant over the years 1829 to 1831, shows the flagpoles north of the lighthouse going almost down to the road from Moreton to Birkenhead through

Bidston Village, while those to the south are marked well beyond the windmill and almost to the old road from Upton to Birkenhead, which climbed the steep Thermopolae Pass before the present road up Ford Hill was constructed. [11]

Holdens, a publisher of tide tables from the late eighteenth century, used a sketch of the flags as the heading for its tide tables.

The flags on Bidston Hill continued in use until the semaphore system, starting in 1827, began to supersede them.

It was at this time, ironically, that Mr. Vyner felt that his "nominal" five shillings per year rent from the ship-owners was a rather poor return on his land, bearing in mind that the owners were saving considerable insurance by their early knowledge of arrivals. In 1830 he attempted to raise the rent to twenty shillings per pole per year. While some owners complied happily, others were reluctant, and Mr. Vyner's agent consulted a solicitor as to whether some poles could be removed without notice because of non-payment. (The original letter and solicitor's reply are amongst the Vyner papers housed at Cheshire Record Office). The solicitor indicated that the ship-owners were entitled to "a notice to quit", and poles should only be removed by Mr. Vyner after a reasonable time had elapsed. [12]

A few posts survived until the 1860s, by which time the electric telegraph was, in turn, superseding the semaphore system (see Chapter Three).

Writing in 1891, Prime Minister Gladstone recalled "the

name of Bidstone from a period considerably beyond 70 years." The row of flags could be seen from number 62 Rodney Street, Liverpool, where he had been born in 1809. At that time the flag representing his father's company could be seen at position seven in the line running south from the lighthouse.

It is still possible to see evidence of the flag system on Bidston Hill in the form of a number of the sockets in which the flagpoles stood.

The 30 cm (12 inch) ruler gives an indication of the size of the posthole.

The holes cut into the rock to support the flagpoles were usually round, about 30 cm in diameter, and had smaller square holes nearby, in which the oblique wooden supports of the flagpoles were wedged. Most of the holes have long since disappeared under the spread of greenery on the hill, but at least three complete holes, where flagstaffs were erected, can be seen in the rock of the hill-top. One is about 20 metres from the windmill, and is signposted by the rangers. The second is a square support hole, and is located about 30 metres further along the path towards the observatory. The best example is round (see photo), usually water-filled, and set in the rock about 150 metres south of the observatory. All three holes are on the western side of the hill-top. There are several half circles (see photos) carved into the west-facing rock between the windmill and the Observatory. Some holes still bear the marks made by the stonemason's tools.

(The 30 cm ruler gives an indication of size).

It would obviously have been easier to carve half-circles into the side of the rocks, than to carve full circles down into the rock surface.

Chapter Two

Bidston Lighthouse

The first lighthouse to be built in England was probably the one erected at The Lizard in Cornwall by Sir John Killigrew in 1619. He built it at his own expense, and attempted to pay for its upkeep by collecting voluntary contributions from the owners of passing ships. However the money was not forthcoming, and Sir John was threatened with bankruptcy. The lighthouse was subsequently pulled down.[1]

In 1664, a Mr. Reading applied for a patent to enable him to erect lighthouses on the West Coast of England and to levy a toll for their maintenance.[2] This caused great alarm in Liverpool. Perhaps the Mayor and Corporation saw it as a loss of possible income to the city, but their concern may have been purely for the safety of shipping. In early days the lighthouse illumination was created by a fire burning in an open grate on top of a wooden structure. Wreckers were liable to start fires on the coast merely to confuse seamen and deliberately cause them to steer their vessels onto rocks or sandbanks, and the Wirral coast had a reputation for being infested with wreckers. Whatever the reason, the Corporation of Liverpool asked its representative, Sir Gilbert Ireland, to present a petition to Parliament opposing the patent. The actual wording of the correspondence and petition makes fascinating reading: -

Letter to Sir Gilbert Ireland:-

"Sir, Yesterday we received a copie of the Ord^r inclosed. In regard those lighthouses will be no benefit to our Mariners, but a hurt, & expose them to more danger if trust to them and also to be a very great and unnecessary burden and charge to them.
Wee are S^r
Yo^r most humble servants
Thomas Johnson (Mayor)
Thomas Ayndoe (Mayor in 1655)
Henry Corless (Mayor in 1661)
John Sturzaker
Thomas Bickersteth
Liverpoole 5th Jan 1664"

The petition presented to Parliament read:-

"22 August 16 Charles II *
At an Assemblie & C 'It is ordered that a Peticon by framed in the name of the Merchants, Owners of Shipps, & Seamen of this burrough, to oppose a Bill intended to be exhibited in the next P'liamt, a draught or copie whereof is sent to us by or worthie & honerable Member & burges in P'liamt for this Corporacon, Sr Gilbert Ireland & now read unto us, being for the p'tended erecting & setting up of lighthouses within the range of the Redd Chanell, to testify our utter dislike thereof,

& disowninge anie of oure consent thereunto, as in the same draught is pretended untruely."[3]

* There is some question as to the actual date of the petition - 1664 or 1670? However, the entry in the Liverpool Town Books gives the date of the petition as "22 August 16 Charles II" (i.e. 22nd August in the 16th year of the reign of Charles II). The system of dating was calculated as the number of years since the start of the reign of the current monarch. Although Charles II was not restored to the English throne till 1670 he had, acording to royalists, become monarch on the day following his father's execution, i.e. 31st January 1649. On this basis the 16th year of his reign was 1664.

The petition was apparently successful because it was another hundred years before lighthouses were erected in the vicinity of Liverpool.

However Mr. Reading and friends did not take defeat lightly. In 1668 the King granted a patent for the building of a lighthouse at St. Ann's Head, near Milford Haven. This light, meant to be supported by voluntary contribution, was discontinued when the proprietors were found to be illegally extracting dues from shipowners.

Parliament dealt with further trouble in 1670. An entry in the House of Commons Journal reads (under the heading: "Lighthouses in Ireland - 8th April 1670"),
"A petition of the Owners and Masters of Ships belonging to Chester, Liverpoole, and ports adjacent, complaining of a great Grievance and Exaction, by the Patentees of the Light-

houses, in demanding and receiving Fees for Tonnage upon Ships, a yearly Imposition on Fisher-boats, and Twelve-pence the Head on Passengers, was read and debated."

"Resolved - That the Petition be referred to the Committee of Grievance, to take the matter of the Petition and Grievance therein complained of, into their Consideration, the first Wednesday of their meeting and sitting after the recess (the recess lasted from May to October): that a Copy of the Petition, together with this Order, be sent to the Patentees, or the Officers and Agents by them employed, that they may take notice thereof: And Mr. Stanley is desired to take care to see them conveyed."[4]

Result: - Order of Parliament
"Lune 19e die Decembris 1670
Ordered - That the Committee of Grievances doe sitt vpon Wednesday moneth next, & doe examine the matter of Grievance formerly Complayned of against Mr. Reading & others by peticon referred to the said Committee. And that Mr. Reading doe cause notice to be sent to the Parties concerned.
William Goldsborough
Cler. Dom. Com.
This is A true Coppy of ye oridginall order."

In 1690 William III and his army embarked for Ireland from Hyle Lake. At this stage Hyle Lake was half a mile wide, 15 feet deep at its western end and 30 feet deep at the eastern end. (By 1840 sandbanks had spread to such an extent that the lake had shrunk to a width of 140 yards. The depth was 2 feet at the eastern end and it was dry at the western end).[5]

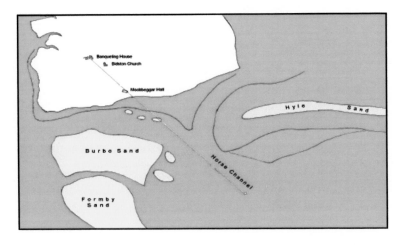

This sketch is taken from a Dutch map dated 1700, one of the earliest maps of the region in existence.[6]

Then, in August 1759, the Common Council of the Borough of Liverpool ordered that "A floating light be fixed where the North East Buoy of Hoyl now lies, and that the Buoy which now lies there should be laid upon the Spitt to the Eastward of Helbry Swash", and that "the Landmark leading into Hoyl Lake be either raised or first white washed or rough cast on the upper part as it's not plainly seen from the Buoy, it lying under the high land."[7]

On August 10th 1762, an act was passed empowering the Corporation of Liverpool, as distinct from the Dock Trustees, to construct lighthouses where necessary for the navigation of the entrances to the port.

At that time the route into Liverpool for shipping was via the Horse Channel into the anchorage at Hoyle Lake, then hugging the North Wirral Coast to Dove Point, seaward of the present Meols, rounding the point at New Brighton and crossing the river to Liverpool. Then, as now, sandbanks were a hazard and shipping had to follow the channels closely in order to avoid running aground.

In 1763 two lighthouses were built at Mockbeggar (Leasowe), two others at Hoylake. If navigators kept the first two lights, known as Sea Lights, in alignment, they could sail safely through the Horse Channel. When the two lights at Hoylake, the Lake Lights, came into alignment, the ship could change course and find safe anchorage in the deeper Hoyle Lake. Some off-loading often took place, in order that, the following day, the vessels, having been relieved of some of their cargo, could weigh anchor and sail round the Wirral Coast to Liverpool (over the flatts).

The inner Lake Light at Hoylake was a brick tower, painted red and more than 60 feet high, while the outer one was white and only 25 feet high. This outer light was built of wood, resembling a giant lantern, and was movable, to allow for the frequently shifting sands in the entrance channel.

The inner Sea Light at Leasowe was black and white, about 100 feet high. The outer one, like Hoylake's, was only 25 feet high and was supposedly movable.

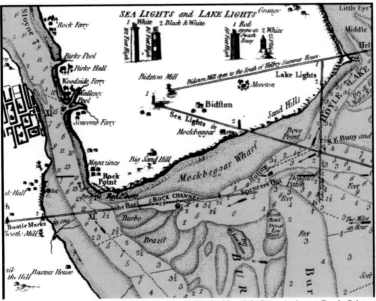

This sketch is taken from a "New Chart of the West Coast of England from Point Lynas, Anglesey to Formby Point, Lancashire" 1783, showing the Sea Lights and the Lake Lights.
(Courtesy Williamson Art Gallery - Birkenhead)[8]

William Hutchinson (1715-1801) was a colourful character, born in Newcastle on Tyne, who had followed a sea-faring life since the age of 15. He started as a cook's cabin boy and beer drawer, and later became a successful privateer. He was second in command to Fortunatus Wright, a well-known privateer, on the brigantine "Fame." However "The old, rough pattern of privateer conmmander had begun to give way to an educated and public spirited type of officer who did more thinking and less cursing and was at least the equal of the average naval officer of the period in intelligence and bravery. Of such men were Fortunatus Wright, William Hutchinson ...." [9]

In 1761, after deciding to abandon this way of life and settle down in Liverpool, Hutchinson was appointed keeper of the buoys in the area, and became Liverpool's first Dockmaster and Water Bailiff, a position he held for more than 40 years. In this capacity he searched for a safer method of providing lighthouse beams than that provided by a coal or wood fire, and he started to experiment with light enhanced by reflecting mirrors.

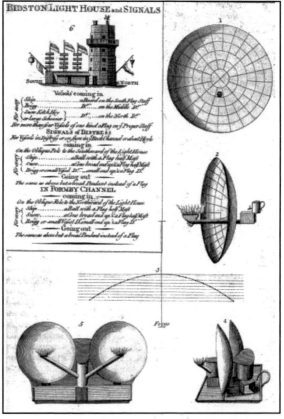

Courtesy of The Science Museum[10]

He may well have got the idea from a meeting he attended at The Merchants' Coffee House in the town. A colleague was demonstrating how he could read the print of a newspaper placed about 30 feet away in a darkened room. He did this by holding a wooden bowl, lined with tiny pieces of looking glass set in putty, behind a tiny candle.[11] The light from the candle was then concentrated on one small area of the newspaper at a time, and the print became readable. Hutchinson decided to develop the idea, with lighthouses in mind, and found that the shape of the bowl was all-important to concentrating the beam. It had to take the shape of a parabola, less curved towards the edges (see drawings). A light was duly erected at Bidston, possibly on the roof of the wooden flag-signal building, and Captain Hutchinson's first reflecting mirror lights were installed about 1763. The light came from lamps burning behind glass. The first mirror consisted of tinned plates soldered together. Hutchinson later improved on his first parabolic reflector by devising one lined with pieces of mirror. Those inventions are described in detail by Hutchinson, with illustrations, in the fourth edition of his Treatise.

In 1763, the Bidston light must have been purely experimental, as the wrecking of the Outer Light at Mockbeggar and Liverpool Corporation's subsequent idea of erecting a lighthouse on Bidston Hill was still a matter for the future. Maybe for this experiment Hutchinson's light was directed to shine inland, so as not to confuse seafarers. Or it is possible that he soon realised that Bidston Hill was in line with the Mockbeggar lights, and for a few years three lights may have come into line for ships approaching the coast. There doesn't seem to have been any great sense of urgency over replacing the wrecked sea light at Mockbeggar in 1771, so very possibly Hutchinson's light was already shining out in line with the Inner Sea Light. It was found to be 200 times stronger than the old light at Everton Beacon (see Chapter Three), and this greatly enhanced illumination helped to curtail the activities of the notorious Leasowe wrecking gangs.

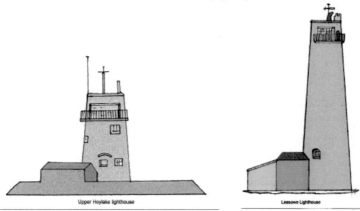

Upper Hoylake lighthouse

Leasowe Lighthouse

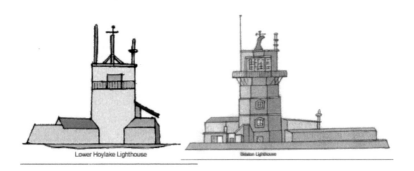

Lower Hoylake Lighthouse

Bidston Lighthouse

The four lighthouse diagrams are based on sketches in "Sailing Instructions from Point Lynas to Liverpool."[12]

On February 1st 1764 the Liverpool Town Council ordered that "Alexander Smarley, John Bennett and Samuel Ainsdell be appointed Persons to attend the Lighthouses or to make the Light fires there and to do other necessary duty there .... and that their Salary be twenty pounds a year each, to be paid monthly, and that the Committee have power to suspend them or any of them for breach or neglect of duty, such offenders to be reported to the next Council."[13]

A few weeks later, on April 16th, the order was amended - "And whereas it is found that the duty and other inconveniences attending the two lights near Mockbeggar greatly exceed those at Hoyl lake, that the two Lightmen appointed to the first mentioned Lights be paid twenty-two pounds a year each and that the other two at Hoyl lake eighteen pounds a year each and that Alexander Smarley and John Bennett be appointed to the Lights near Mockbeggar and Jeremiah (Samuel?) Ainsdell and Thomas Rimmer at the Lights near Hoyl Lake."

The light provided by iron braziers burning, at first, wood, then later, coal, meant that the intensity of the light beams varied quite a bit. If the coalfire had been recently banked up there would be very little light, and if the fire flamed too strongly, especially in strong winds, there was danger of melting of the braziers and consequently setting fire to the wooden buildings. This actually happened on several occasions. Captain Hutchinson noted that one of the Hoylake lights was burned on 15 July 1765, and there was a strong tradition that the interior of the Leasowe lighthouse was later burned out. At a Council Meeting on October 2nd 1765, it was ordered that: "Richard Welding be allowed and paid by the Treasurer of the Light Duties the sum of sixty pounds towards the loss he sustained by the accidental burning down of one of the Lighthouses in Cheshire and that the Treasurer of the said Duties be allowed the same in his accounts, and that no Ale or other Liquors be allowed to be sold in any of the said Lighthouses."[14] Could a state of inebriation have contributed to the cause of the fire?

There is another strong tradition that the outer lighthouse at Mockbeggar was movable, made of wood and erected on the shore. Sometime around 1771 it was lost. What actually happened is uncertain. It seems to have been either found unusable due to coastal erosion or it was washed away. There is no doubt that erosion was a problem. As far back as 1749 J.Robert Vyner had visited the area in response to concern, expressed by some of his tenants, about erosion. A letter in his own handwriting, dated August 24th 1749 says: "I Robert Vyner, being at Bidstone, and some of the Tennants having expressed an apprehension that the Sea gathered fast upon the Leasow, I obtained from Mr. Hoss the heir of the Meols family, a sight of the Map of his Estate and of his Common called the Claryl, which we guessed to have been made about 1690." [15] This showed that there had been considerable erosion of the coastline between 1690 and 1749.

A report says that in May 1773 the outer lighthouse at Mockbeggar still stood, but was 'decayed' - 600 yards NW of the present light, i.e. it was a quarter mile out to sea from the present high water level.[16] A ninety year old fisherman, John Edwards, who had lived all his life on Wirral coast, when speaking in 1856 to Mr. Rollett, who was at that time in charge of the Leasowe embankment, recalled that, as a young boy he saw the old lighthouse "being washed down", and recalled the wooden outbuildings "being floated on the shore." Then in 1865-66 it was written that: "The remains of the old lighthouse, to seaward, have been seen by several persons now alive."

Liverpool Corporation was reluctant to throw good money after bad by building yet another vulnerable lighthouse on or near the same spot, but it was quickly realised that the pre-existing wooden tower on Bidston Hill, where Captain Hutchinson was already experimenting with reflecting mirrors, was in the same alignment with the inner Leasowe Sea Light as the wrecked one had been. Consequently a light on Bidston Hill would give safe guidance to approaching vessels, so long as they kept it lined up above the Leasowe light until the Hoylake lights came into alignment.

On June 5th 1771 the Dock Committee was "authorised and appointed to treat with Mr. Vyner about the Scite and Erection of a Light House on Bidston Hill and to Build a Light House there". Agreement was reached.[17]

A "parcel of land, 30 yards square, was leased to the Mayor, Baillifs and Burgesses for the purpose of building a light house for the term of 60 years." The rent was 20 shillings.

The painting, by Saloman, dated 1825, shows the old Bidston lighthouse and some of the flagpoles.
(Courtesy National Museums Liverpool)

The new building was octagonal, made of stone, about 55 feet high and with an outside gallery running right round the lantern room (not unlike the present tower). It was "frequently taken for a church." A cowl was fixed to the lead roof and a copper flue pipe extracted fumes from the oil light and ventilated the lantern room. The lighthouse had adjoining cottages for the keeper and his assistant, and it contained Hutchinson's reflectors, which had now evidently been improved on by a Mr. Holden and which had also been installed in the other lighthouses. In July 1772 the Council ordered that "the sum of Twenty Guineas be given to Mr. Holden for his invention of the Reflecting Lights fixed up at the Lighthouses for this Port and to be paid him by Mr. Gerard the Receiver out of this Duty in full of all demands on the Trustees of the said Duties."[18]

Liverpool Council was anxious to protect its interests. On January 3rd 1776 it was "Resolved and Ordered by this Council that this Corporation as Trustees of the Docks and Lighthouses do oppose a Bill intended to be brought into Parliament by the Citizens and Traders of Chester for erecting Lighthouses on the Point of Air and other purposes, the same being detrimental to the Navigation of this Town and Port, and that the Committee of Trade be desired to watch the Motions of the Promoters of such Bill." Despite this opposition a private lighthouse was erected at Point of Air under grant of 1775-76 and leased by Chester Corporation. It was lit by oil lamps or candles. In 1818 the Northern Lighthouse Board replaced it with a lighthouse designed by Robert Stevenson using argand lamps and 2-foot reflectors.

Pirates posed a problem for the authorities in the 18th Century. During the American War of Independence one particular privateer, the American Captain John Paul Jones, cruised the Irish Channel, terrorising shipping off the west coast of England and Scotland. He set fire to the vessels in Whitehaven Harbour, but evaded all attempts at capture by taking refuge in French or Dutch ports. In 1778 he was sighted off the west coast of England, heading a flotilla of pirate vessels in his ship 'Providence'. Liverpool Town Council called a special meeting to find the most effective way of defending Liverpool against Paul Jones or any other invader. An order was issued to the following effect: "That Richard Wilding, upon any Intelligence of an Enemy, give an Alarm at Bidston Lighthouse; and not keep the Lights burning either there or at Hoylake in such case", and, amongst other orders, that "A pilot boat be sent out to cruise off Point Lynas, to give intelligence upon the appearance of an enemy", and that "boats be stationed at the different buoys along the coast to sink them in case of imminent danger." To everybody's relief Captain Jones did not sail towards Liverpool.[19]

Richard Wilding may have been the Richard Welding who had received compensation following the Hoylake lighthouse fire in 1765. It is possible he held a managerial position supervising all four lighthouses.

In a letter written in May 1773, John Phillips, Dock Master of the North Dock, voiced his disapproval of lighthouses being placed on hills some distance inland, particularly the one built on Bidston Hill in 1771 to replace the Outer Sea Light at Leasowe. Here are some of his objections: "that every intention of a Lighthouse and Landmark is materially prevented, not to say defeated, by the situation, and I might add by the construction of the one on Bidston Hill, though the defects in construction may be dispensed with ….. … the higher the elevation, the greater distance they can be seen, but the higher they are the more they are involved in an opacious atmosphere, in foggy and hazy weather; it is the safe, and not the great distance that is wanted …….. It will be worse than trifling unless the tower on Bidston Hill is entirely demolished, and another built whereabouts the old decayed one stands (on the seashore), or as near it as to retain all its advantages."[20]

His complaints fell on deaf ears, for the structure on Bidston Hill was to stand for another hundred years.

Even in those days vandalism could be a problem. A press report of 1782 noted:

"Some evil disposed person wilfully broke seven panes in the lower light of the wooden lighthouse at Hoylake with stones."

Shortly afterwards the outer light at Hoylake was replaced by a permanent brick structure (presumably the shifting sands were now considered more stable) which was sited at the shore end of the present Alderney Road.

The Royal Hotel at "High Lake" was completed in 1792. Unfortunately, sometimes the hotel lights were mistaken by ships' crews for those of the Hoyle Lake lighthouse, which prompted the Liverpool Dock Board to send a notice to the hotel, headed "Caution," and showing a picture of old Hoyle Lake lighthouse, with the lifeboat going to a ship sinking in the distance. Below the drawing was written the following:-

"THE TRUSTEES

OF THE

LIVERPOOL DOCKS AND HARBOUR,

on whom, in that capacity, the care and management of the Hoyle Lake lighthouses devolve, have been informed of frequent instances of the lights in the rooms of the Hoyle Lake Hotel having been mistaken for those of the lighthouse, whereby several vessels have run on shore, and the lives and property of many individuals have been exposed to the most imminent danger; the Trustees have therefore to request that it may become the invariable rule of the Hoyle Lake Hotel that the window shutters of the rooms which front the sea be closed every evening immediately on the introduction of fire or candle light, a custom which they feel confident will be cheerfully and punctually pursued when thus recommended by the powerful motives of humanity."

The master of the hotel, Richard Brotherton, assured the trust that "the necessary orders were being enforced in the principles of philanthropy and humanity."[21]

Robert Stevenson, the engineer noted for building many of Scotland's lighthouses, in particular the Bell Rock, was the grandfather of the author Robert Louis Stevenson. In 1801 Robert (the engineer) made a tour, the first of three, round the coast of England, visiting many lighthouses including Wirral Sea Lights and Lake Lights. Of all those he inspected he was complimentary about only two, and one of those was at Bidston.

To quote him - "This lighthouse is remarkably well taken care of - being in every respect clean and in good order." He noted that: "The light from Bidston is from oil with one reflector of silvered glass, which is no less than thirteen and a half feet diameter and its focus four feet. This immense reflector is illuminated by one large flat cotton wick which consumes one gallon of oil in four hours." Stevenson felt that this was an excessive use of oil.

To quote him - "I cannot see any good reason for expending such a quantity of oil for one reflector as the same quantity would answer for thirty reflectors of twenty inches diameter, and I am confident that seven such reflectors would give an equal if not superior light. Probably it may have been thought, as the light is wanted in the same direction with the rays of the Sea light, that therefore there ought to be but one reflector in each lighthouse. This, however, is proceeding upon a mistake, as seven or greater number of reflectors may be so set that their rays shall have an identical path."[22]

He added:- "Each of the four lighthouses had one keeper, and although the Lake Lights, being only 500 paces apart, could have been managed by one person, it was preferred to employ two, at equal salaries, as a check upon each other."

The oil wick at Bidston was 14 inches wide and was made from cotton thread ¼ inch thick. The keeper was required to snuff the lamp every 3 or 4 hours. To avoid the risk of fire and ensure his own safety, he used long pincers to draw the wick through the burner tube, and cut it with a pair of shears held in the other hand. The snuffings were then dropped into a container of water.[23]

Oil lamps were still not very satisfactory. A Mr. Drummond, who may have seen the Bidston reflector in use, noted in 1830 that the volume of smoke rising from the oil lamp completely blocked out the light from the upper part of the reflector, but in 1847 it was claimed that the lights at Bidston and Leasowe were visible from a circle of 14 miles.[24]

In 1827 Mr. Vyner sold an area of 157 acres, including the lighthouse site, to the Liverpool Dock Trustees for the sum of £10,260. The rent for the windmill site was two guineas per annum. (This was the time when Mr. Vyner took the opportunity to increase the charge for flagpoles from 5 shillings to 20 shillings per annum.)

Ann Urmson was appointed keeper of the Bidston Light in 1835 at the age of 30. Her younger sister Catharine joined her in the duties, and they were paid a joint salary of £73-10s per annum plus 15 tons of coal. Ann received a letter on the subject of coal from William Lord, the Marine Surveyor, in November 1838 which read:

"Miss Urmson,

I am desired by Captain Denham to forward to you the enclosed order for two tons of coal, and to inform you that you are no longer to supply coal for the Telegraph (see next chapter). Your coal order for this year amounts to 26 tons, and he desires me to say that for the future you must be restricted to the same allowance as the other lighthouses which averages 14 tons per year."[25]

Following the severe storm of January 1839 (see chapter on Meteorology) William Lord reported to the Observatory Committee that "the roof of the washhouse and those of the sitting room and outbuildings of Bidston Lighthouse are very much damaged and cause them much inconvenience as they inhabit the kitchen which is adjacent to the washhouse and the rain and snow drive in. The door of the coalhouse is also blown away."[26]

In the summer of 1841 Catharine Urmson was about to be married, and she requested that her future husband John Urmson (a cousin perhaps?) be allowed to live in a lighthouse cottage. This was granted on the condition that he produce "a certificate of his character" (this was duly written by John Deane Case Esq.), and John was also required to enter into a "Warrant of Ejectment" whereby he agreed to "quit and deliver possession whenever required."[27] The Internet (1837online) reveals that Ann Urmson, Catharine Urmson and John Urmson were all married on Wirral in the summer of 1841. Catharine died in 1846 and the 1851 census shows that Ann was married to John Urmson who was now assistant lighthouse keeper at Bidston. It may be that Ann's first husband had also died, and she had subsequently married Catherine's widower. However I can find no record of such a marriage.

In September 1862 it was recommended that a new lighthouse be erected in place of the Upper Hoylake Lighthouse together with a house for the keeper at a cost of about £840, and that necessary alterations be made at the Lower Lighthouse, estimated cost £225.

Ann Urmson died in 1869 and this "afforded opportunity to effect the amalgamation of Bidston Lighthouse and Telegraph [see next chapter] Establishments."

Bidston lighthouse and cottages re-built in 1872.

John Urmson was appointed Principal Assistant Keeper of the new system at £50 per annum plus uniform and 12 tons of coal.

In 1870 the Marine Surveyor reported on the condition of Bidston Lighthouse. A Royal Commission on Lights, Buoys and Beacons had reported that the reflectors compared unfavourably with other lighthouses due to age and wear. Part of the lighthouse buildings had been pulled down when the new Observatory was built. The Marine Surveyor was asked to confer with the Engineer and prepare estimates for the cost of repair or replacement of the lighthouse, of adapting the tower to modern Dioptic Apparatus, and of rebuilding the keepers' cottages which adjoined the lighthouse.[28]

The door of Bidston Lighthouse showing the words: 'Mersey Dock Estate' and the date 1873.

In February 1872 it was recommended that the existing cottages be replaced by three new ones at an estimated cost of £1475. The new lighthouse would cost £970, with the light room window accounting for £200. Messrs Chance Bros and Co. were to provide the Dioptic A light at a cost of £1600. The estimates were accepted and building went ahead. While the new lighthouse was being erected, a temporary light was displayed on the roof of the old Telegraph Office. John Urmson, now aged 65, was "to be retained at the temporary light so long as may be necessary for the services of that light and on his services being discontinued he be granted a retiring allowance of 10 shillings per week."

A new telegraph system was installed in the lighthouse, and a stone wall was built on the west and north sides of the lighthouse using "a quantity of stone lying on the ground at Bidston, which has been quarried in forming the roads."

All of these substantial buildings are still standing in the 21st Century.

The diagrams below, based on original Ordnance Survey maps dated 1872 and 1909 show the relative positions of the old and new lighthouses at Bidston.[29]
The old lighthouse appears to have been closer to the

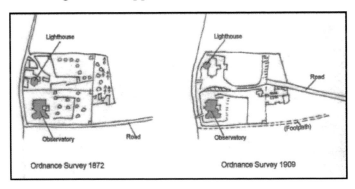

Observatory than the new one by a distance of about 50 feet. This seems to be confirmed by a quote from Captain Graham Hill's account of Bidston Lighthouse history: "The first Bidston Lighthouse was a few yards to the Southward of the existing tower." A fence separated the lighthouse site from the Observatory. No indication of the old site remains - it is lost under the tarmac roadway. Presumably the slight change of angle resulting from the re-siting of the lighthouse was not sufficient to affect the alignment of the Sea Lights through Leasowe Lighthouse.

In 1886 it was reported to the Mersey Docks and Harbour Board (MDHB) that the gardens attached to Bidston and Point Lynas lighthouses and telegraph stations were not as productive as those at Leasowe and Crosby due to the nature of the soil. As a result it was resolved to recommend an allowance of £2 per annum to John. E. Hughes and Richard Roberts, who were keepers at Bidston and Point Lynas respectively.

As a system of lighted buoys came into use, and the shipping route into the Mersey via the Crosby Channel gradually gained preference over the North Wirral coastal route, the need for the Wirral lighthouse system declined.

The upper Hoylake light, in Valentia Road, was last lit on 14th May 1886, whilst the lower light was extinguished on 14th July 1908. Permission to convert the lighthouse in Valentia Road to a dwelling house was refused in October 1898, but the Dock Board relented a year later, and the premises were let to Mr.T.J. Walmsley. The rent was to be £52-10-0 per annum until the light was removed and £54-0-0 thereafter. This lighthouse was sold in 1909 to Captain Wheeler, the Superintendent of Pilotage. He lived there for a number of years. The lighthouse is still a private residence in the 21st century. The lower Hoylake lighthouse was pulled down in the

Hoylake lower light shown on a postcard dated 1916.

1920s to make way for the Winter Gardens cinema, which regrettably no longer exists.

The Leasowe light was extinguished on 15th July 1908, and the lighthouse was sold to Wallasey Corporation in 1930. For a long time it was disused, but in recent years it has been extensively renovated by the Friends of Leasowe Lighthouse, and is regularly open to the public.

The MDHB Committee decided that the Bidston light would be switched off after sunrise on 9th October 1913, and that the use of the Bidston lighthouse as a telegraph station should be discontinued at the same time. Charles Stanford was the lighthouse and telegraph keeper at the time of closure. In July 1914 the Honorary Secretary of the Committee of Management, Bidston Hill Recreation Ground, offered to take a tenancy of the Bidston Lighthouse and Telegraph Station at a rental of £50. His offer was accepted.

In July 1934 the Marine Committee decided that Bidston Lighthouse and Telegraph Station should be offered for sale to Birkenhead Corporation and a price of £1500 should be quoted. However, under a conveyance drawn up in April 1935, the Dock Board offered the lighthouse, together with the cottages and 5038 square yards of land for sale to Birkenhead Council for the smaller sum of £1000 on the understanding that the Council "maintain the accommodation roadway leading to, and between, this property and the Bidston Observatory."[30] The sale went ahead. Moving the adaptation of the minutes of the Estate and Development Committee of Birkenhead Council, Mr. Egan felt that "the Corporation had a real feeling of gratitude to the MDHB for the magnanimous way in which they had met the Corporation. They wanted considerably more for the property and if they had put it out in the market would probably have got it. By this purchase the land would be available for all future generations for recreational purposes."

Birkenhead Council had recently purchased part of Bidston Hill from Mr. Vyner. The cottages were rented out to employees of Birkenhead Council. Mick Connell, a bowling green keeper with the Council, moved into one of the cottages with his family in 1937. For a time the lighthouse was used by radio operators. When the Natural Environment Research Council (NERC) took over control of the Observatory in 1969, one cottage continued to be rented out to the Connell family, but the other two were converted into offices. In those days the lighthouse was largely used for storage of NERC property. The elevation of the lighthouse again proved useful in 1999 when the Wirral Amateur Radio Society operated from the lamp room for a time. In recent years members of the Observatory staff, with grants, have renovated the lighthouse, and both Observatory staff and Wirral Borough Council open it up to the public from time to time. To mark the Millennium, local schools were invited to design a light for the Observatory, to line up with that of Leasowe, as in the old days. The winning light, designed by Hilbre High School, is still lit each evening from 6 pm to 10 pm, operated by wind power.

Chapter Three

Semaphore Station

In 1792, following the Revolution, six French brothers, surname Clappe, invented a signalling system to pass messages between towers set nine or ten miles apart.[1]

Two years later the Rev. John Gamble, Chaplain to the Duke of York, having observed the French signals, designed a vertical frame system for use in England. This frame contained five shutters. By a combination of open and closed shutters 31 signs could be transmitted across the miles. Unbeknown to Rev. Gamble, the Rev. Lord George Murray, a son of the third Duke of Atholl, was, at the same time, designing a more sophisticated six-shutter model which could transmit 63 signs.

In 1795 the Admiralty set up a line of 48 signal towers for defence purposes along the South Coast of England from Land's End to Sheerness. These stations had only limited communication using a system of balls and flags. The Admiralty decided to replace this system with one of the more superior shutter systems. Much to the frustration of Rev. Gamble, they chose to adopt Lord Murray's model.

This resulted in shutter telegraph lines being set up between London and Chatham, London and Portsmouth, London and Plymouth, and, by 1808, London and Yarmouth.

The government of the day also thought it desirable to establish a signal station in Liverpool to communicate with the lighthouse at Bidston so that "earliest confirmation of any hostile prowlers off the (Irish Sea) coast" might be obtained.[2] The Bidston station appears to have been sited immediately south of the windmill, although the lighthouse could display flags indicating "Enemies" and "Men of War."

A wooden signal station was erected on the site of the Old Beacon Tower in Everton with a wooden cottage built alongside for the signal master's use. There had been a tower in Everton as far back as 1230, when Ranulf, Earl of Chester, was given control of Liverpool by Henry III.[3] The Beacon Tower stood on the highest point of the East Ridge in Everton for nearly six hundred years and commanded views of the beacons on Billinge Hill and Ashhurst Hill. In clear weather Black Combe in the Southern Lake District was visible to the north, and Moel Fammau and the Denbighshire Range were visible to the west and south, with Beeston Castle in the distance. The Beacon Tower was built of red sandstone, covering an area 18 feet square, and was 25 to 30 feet in height. It was built in two storeys with a raised turret at one end, holding a receptacle for the faggots and brushwood used for the beacon fire.[4] The Tower was marked on John Eyes' Survey of the Sea-Coast from Chester Bar to Formby Point, printed in 1755.

More signal stations were erected along the North Wales Coast at the instigation of Prince William, later to be William IV.[5] The resulting eight stations were Everton (St. Domingo), Bidston, Point of Air, Cave Hill, Great Orme's Head, Table Hill, Point Lynas and Holyhead. Each station consisted of a wooden hut, a 30 foot flagstaff and a 30 foot gaff yard. Signals were made to vessels at sea using the Admiralty Ball and Flag system. The signal master could send messages to ships off the coast using an Admiralty code, giving details such as location, or the whereabouts of enemy vessels. At that stage the ships' masters apparently had no means of replying to the messages.

A "veteran", Lieutenant James Watson R.N. was appointed as signal master at Everton in 1804, and held the position until the declaration of peace, in 1815, rendered the system obsolete.[6] Following the cessation of war, the shutter lines in the South of England were no longer required, and by 1816 all these lines had been closed down.

Meanwhile the method of flagpole communication between Liverpool ship owners and the lookout at Bidston continued. Under this system only company house flags could be signalled between Bidston and Liverpool, but it was realised that if a lookout stationed at Holyhead on Anglesey was able to note the actual name of an approaching vessel and quickly dispatch this information to Liverpool, the ship owner would have considerably more time to prepare for the arrival of that specific vessel. Consequently a new system of communication was put into effect.

Each vessel which sailed into Liverpool was allocated a three figure number. A series of ten different flags was designed to represent the numbers 0 - 9 (see sketch), and the ships hoisted the flags corresponding to their numbers ("making their numbers") as they approached Anglesey.[7]

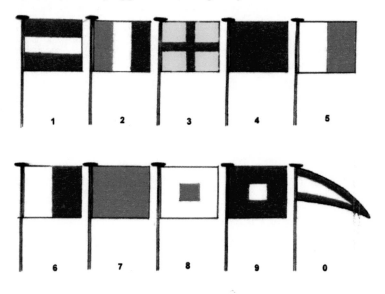

So now, rather than flying just one flag indicating ownership, each vessel was required to fly three flags. The lookout at Holyhead was provided with a list of vessels and their corresponding numbers. He observed the flags hoisted at the masts, looked up the number and name, and the information was then conveyed to the ship owner in Liverpool by the regular post. Here the system failed somewhat, because transmission by regular post, presumably on horseback, meant that it could be 24 hours or more before the news reached Liverpool. This was purely a local arrangement in that it applied only to vessels known in Liverpool. It had the added advantage that vessels which did not hoist known flags would be immediately identified as strangers, possibly with hostile intentions, and suitable precautions could be taken.

It had been intended that each ship be supplied with a full set of ten flags at a cost of eight guineas, but it seems likely that in most cases the owners provided only the three flags representing the vessel's identity, at a more reasonable cost of £2-5s. A copy of the vocabulary was priced at 12/6d.[8]

The Admiralty, and in particular Sir Hume Popham (1762 -1820), was taking a new interest in the French semaphore masts. Many of the former coastal stations were converted from the use of balls and flags, to a semaphore system, similar to the French one, but using two arms mounted on a single post rather than three, and using chains (similar to bicycle chains) rather than ropes. The wooden masts were 30 feet high.[9]

Popham also designed a smaller semaphore system for use on ships. This consisted of two masts, each only 12 feet high, which could be moved on trolleys about the decks, and be fastened to the bulwarks. He produced a signal code for use with the masts, improving on it over a number of years. It became an official Admiralty publication in 1816.
A few years after Popham's death in 1820 the Admiralty decided to abandon his sea telegraph system. They replaced it with one designed by Popham's rival in semaphore design, Charles William Pasley, R.E.

Whereas communication between the Admiralty and naval vessels was necessary during the Napoleonic War, the situation was different for the Mercantile Marine. The war had necessarily restricted communication with merchant vessels because of the risk of information falling into enemy hands. Merchant ships had travelled in convoys, without much need to contact each other, but now that peace was being established, the vessels had more freedom of movement and it was desirable that they should be able to communicate both with each other and with the mainland.

With this in mind, Captain Marryat, a renowned sea captain, later to earn fame for his novels such as "Mr. Midshipman Easy", adapted Popham's semaphore code for the use of the Mercantile Marine in 1817. This involved the use of tall, wooden masts with movable arms attached, erected in prominent positions along the coast where they could be observed through telescopes from distances of up to twenty miles.

To supplement the semaphore arms he designed a series of code flags to be used by merchant ships at sea. Thus the ships' masters could signal messages to the shore or to each other using the flags, and these messages could then be relayed along the coast using the semaphore arms. This system was widely adopted and was used particularly on the south coast of England.

In March 1826 Lieutenant Bernard Lindsey Watson (unrelated to James Watson of Everton as far as we know) was asked to set up a system of semaphore masts similar to that used by Marryat, but designed to operate along the North Wales coast. Ten stations were involved at first. They were:

1. Holyhead
2. Carreglwyd (near Llanfaethlu on Anglesey's west coast).
3. Llaneilian (near Point Lynas).
4. Puffin Island, at the entrance to the Menai Strait.
5. Great Orme's Head
6. Llysfaen, a promontary on the coast of Denbighshire.
7. Voel Nant (near Prestatyn).
8. Hilbre Island
9. Bidston Hill
10. Chapel Street, Liverpool - Messrs. Duncan's Warehouse.

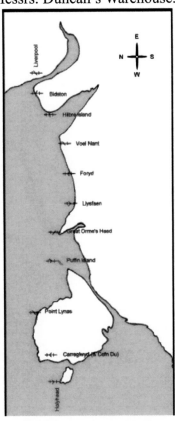

The Liverpool telegraph station was later re-sited on the old churchyard tower. However, a problem arose when messages came through on a Sunday, as some members of the congregation were inclined to hurry out of church in the middle of a service to watch the signals from Bidston.

One reader of the Liverpool Mercury suggested the top of Britannia's dome as a suitable alternative but this idea was rejected.[10] (In January 1849 the station was moved once again, this time to the Tower Buildings near to the river.)

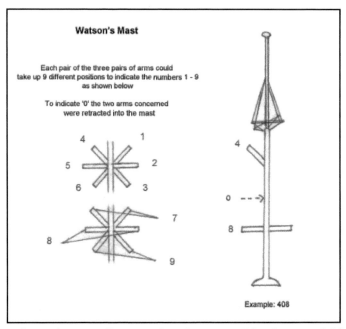

Watson's Mast

Each pair of the three pairs of arms could take up 9 different positions to indicate the numbers 1 - 9 as shown below

To indicate '0' the two arms concerned were retracted into the mast

Example: 408

Foryd, an intermediate station between Llysfaen and Voel Nant, was added on 13th March 1828, as there were visibility problems between the latter two stations.

Lieutenant Watson worked out a vocabulary for the use of the keepers and ships' captains and this was approved by the Dock Committee in March 1827.

Watson's semaphore station consisted of a single wooden mast, 70 feet high, and stayed by four strong chains. The mast had three pairs of semaphore arms, each arm seven and a half feet long, working on pivots and hauled by ropes. The numbers were shown by the signals as above:

To complement the semaphore arms Lieutenant Watson, like

Captain Marryat, designed a flag system for the use of the ships' masters. He continued to use the original flags for the numbers 0 - 9. To change this would have caused confusion and some resentment and extra expense. He introduced two repeater flags: the telegraph flag and the Union Jack.[12]

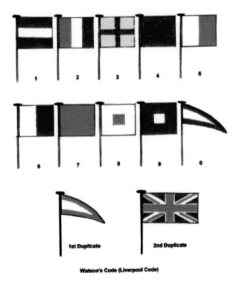

Watson's Code (Liverpool Code)

Thus, if a ship's number contained the same digit twice, or even three times, a duplicate flag was used. Where a number was the same as the one immediately preceding it, the Union Jack was shown. When the number was the same as that two flags above it, the pendant was used (See examples).[13]

Details of Watson's vocabulary apparently no longer exist, but he must have used certain combinations of numbers to represent words or phrases such as "off the head." The ships' masters were equipped with a code book, so that they could interpret the messages being transmitted by the arms.

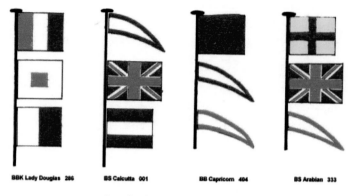

BBK Lady Douglas 286   BS Calcutta 001   BB Capricorn 404   BS Arabian 333

Examples of the Watson (Liverpool) Code

The masters, for their part, communicated with the telegraph keepers and with each other, using the flag code.

In 1828 J. Outram published a numerical list of vessels for the Holyhead-Liverpool Signal Station. The numbers conveyed the identity of approximately 1100 ships, together with their

The photograph shows the surviving telegraph station on Hilbre Island, as it looked in 2002.

tonnage and the master's name. If the semaphore arms failed for any reason the messages could be conveyed by flags instead.[14]

On the Hilbre Island photo note the telescope mountings set into the panoramic window, which faces the Mersey Estuary, Liverpool Bay and the Dee Estuary. The two centre mountings would have been used to view vessels at sea. The right hand one (as we look at it) faces the North Wales coast, and was used to read messages coming in from the Holyhead direction. The left hand one (out of view), facing Bidston, could receive messages from that direction.

This photo of Bidston Lighthouse also shows the remains of telescope fittings in the upper windows.

It was still not possible to eliminate the problems caused by bad weather or during the hours of darkness. One enthusiast wrote to the Liverpool Mercury newspaper, setting out an ingenious system whereby the semaphore arm could be replaced by a set of 25 powerful lamps. However his ideas were rejected on the grounds that, although this might work on a clear night, it would still be ineffective in foggy conditions.

The signallers at each station were paid £40 per annum, and their powerful telescopes cost £10 each.[15] According to a press report of Nov. 16th 1827, the cost of the complete system from Liverpool to Holyhead, including the erection of nine telegraph keepers' houses, was well under £2000. Lieutenant Watson was paid a guinea and a half per day. This was to cover his salary and travelling expenses.

An advertisment published in the Liverpool Mercury read: "Shortly will be published -

WATSON'S TELEGRAPHIC VOCABULARY adapted for a line of SEMAPHORE TELEGRAPHS from LIVERPOOL to HOLYHEAD, as established by the Trustees of the Liverpool Docks, according to Act of Parliament. Also to enable Vessels to communicate to each other any and every species of Intelligence at Sea. To contain a full description of the Telegraph, the method of making signals and illustrated by several plates, with explanations.
Upwards of 500 copies being already ordered, Merchants and Shipowners wishing to make early application to MR THOMAS KAYE - Castle Street."[16]

The telegraph was opened on Friday 26th October 1827.

The first message received from Holyhead, namely that the American packet ship Napoleon was "off the Head", reached Bidston from Holyhead in 15 minutes, but as the station at Bidston was not quite ready the information had then to be carried to Chapel Street by messenger. This may well have added another two or three hours to the time! [17]
The system was fully operational by Monday 5th November,

and the first report to complete the full distance from Holyhead to Liverpool, 72 miles, was a weather report stating that at nine a.m. on the 6th the wind had changed at the Head from SW to W.[18] Reporting of the weather conditions at Holyhead was to prove useful in giving advance knowledge for ships setting sail from Liverpool, particularly as weather systems in this part of England generally move in from the Irish Sea. The incoming vessels continued to display the three flags indicating their code numbers as they approached Anglesey, but now the information could reach Liverpool in 15 minutes via the semaphore arms, rather than in 24 hours via the regular post.

In September 1828 the Dock Sub-Committee resolved that balls (hoops covered with canvas) to distinguish the classes of vessels be provided and fixed upon each station.

Lieutenant Watson reported to the Dock Sub-Committee Meeting of October 18th 1828 that the following were to be the duties of the Telegraph System:-

"That all kinds of shipping intelligence along the whole coast from Holyhead to Liverpool be speedily reported to the Underwriters and Exchange Rooms"

"That the state of the wind at Holyhead be reported at least twice a day and at every change"

"That the situation of the Liverpool Pilot Boats be reported"

"That any communication from vessels to any of the Telegraph Stations, or from Merchants or Consignees to their vessels when off the coast, be speedily forwarded"

This was approved by the committee.[19]

The Rothesay Castle, a paddle steamer, was wrecked on 17th August 1831, on Dutchman's Bank (The Spit), near Puffin

Island, during a pleasure trip from Liverpool to Beaumaris. The steamer was carrying 150 passengers, mostly visitors to Liverpool, and only 29 of them were rescued. According to Gores Annals of Liverpool 1896 the captain was inebriated. A broadsheet was printed and sold to raise funds for the survivors and families of victims. On the sheet was written: "The sensation produced in Liverpool on Thursday morning by the announcement of this awful catastrophe, was indescribable. It was conveyed through the telegraph; and it is due to this excellent establishment to state that the Intelligence was correctly given hour after hour."[20]

Lieutenant Watson resigned his position following a dispute over the provision of flags. He was accused of setting up a lucrative sideline by supplying flags privately to some customers. In 1838 he moved on to design a semaphore system, extending from Hull to Spurn Head, for the Hull Incorporated Chamber of Commerce and Shipping. This system was opened in 1839, but it actually pre-deceased the Liverpool - Holyhead line by 2 or 3 years.

Locally, the Watson Code was renamed the Liverpool Code, and Watson's responsibilities on the Liverpool-Holyhead system were taken over by Lieutenant William Lord R.N. the Marine Surveyor.

He seems to have been quite a strict disciplinarian. In 1841 the Subcommittee recommended that "the keepers of the Telegraphs at Liverpool and Bidston should not be allowed to make private signals and give communications to private parties without the Authority of the Committee and under the superintendence of the Marine Surveyor."

A message sent to one telegraph keeper at that time reads "I send you by the Amlwch Packet the Telescope which you so carelessly and shamefully broke - Enclosed is the bill for the repairs amounting to £4-14-6, which ought to be deducted from your wages and if any similar circumstances occur I shall give orders to that effect. The false lies which you told Mr. Evan's man about the head part <u>falling off</u> a new glass, renders your conduct still more shameful."

Each semaphore station now comprised two iron masts, only 18 feet high, erected on the flat roofs of the signal stations. Looking westwards from Liverpool, the upper left arm showed 1000s, lower left arm 100s, upper right arm 10s, and lower right arm units. The positions of the arms to indicate the numbers 0-9 were retained (see page 54). Thus a number such as 9588 would appear as:-

A wooden indicator at the top of each mast could be displayed or concealed, indicating if the signals were to be read as a number or as a coded word. Thus the 9999 possible combinations of numbers could be used in four different ways to give a possible 39,996 different messages.[21]

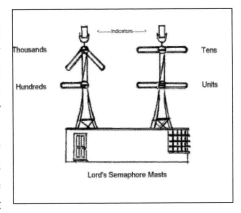

Lord's Semaphore Masts

Example messages are:

1352 Part I "A pilot is aboard"

3557 Part 1 "Has she received much damage?"

1352 Part 2 "Struck by a sea and cargo shifted"

9588 Part 1 "With rudder unshipped"

Observers in Holyhead, reading signals coming from the east, would, of course, read the numbers in reverse. Life must have been a bit more confusing for the intermediate stations, reading signals from both directions, but presumably they soon got used to this.

A letter from William Lord to the Dock Surveyor in June 1839 reports: "At Bidston Telegraph they complain of the roof leaking as they say from the strain brought on it by the new mode of working the arms."[22]

Lieutenant Lord gradually introduced the Marryat Flag Code to bring the local area in line with national usage.

Correspondence in the Marine Surveyor's letter book shows that in September 1841 Captain Woodruff, master of Cunard's first passenger steamship "Britannia" was to use the Holyhead - Liverpool semaphore to communicate with the underwriters' room in Liverpool on the return leg of the maiden voyage.

Using Marryat's Code (M.C.) he would send up to eight signals, namely:

M.C. Part 2 No 530 - "Britannia"

M.C. Part 3 No 421 - "Halifax" (port of origin)

Change to numeric code to display date of sailing, then:

M.C. Part 3 No 2541 - "Great Western" (Steamship)

M.C. Part 3 No 673 - "New York" (port of arrival)

M.C. Part 6 No 169 - "arrived"

Change to numeric code to display date of arrival, or, if necessary, display

M.C. Part 6 No 2079 - "not" before displaying "arrived."

These were the very early days of the contest for the prestigious "Blue Riband of the Atlantic" for passenger steamers sailing between America and Britain, and the Liverpool underwriters would be anxiously waiting to know if Britannia's average speed had beaten that of Brunel's ship "Great Western", which should have reached New York from Bristol shortly before Britannia was due to sail from Halifax to Liverpool on September 4th. It would take Captain Woodruff 20 - 30 minutes to send these signals and there was concern that if the weather was "thick" between Holyhead and Lynas some of the ship's signals might be missed. Contingency plans were made, such that if the messages had been received, the word "communicated" (Marryat Part 6 No 162) would be signalled to Britannia. If "thick" weather obscured the ship's signals, the message "I will attend to your signals" (Marryat Part 4 No 1046) would be signalled from a station where the weather was clear.[23]

In August 1851 while the lighthouse and telegraph station were being painted, a "surgical" certificate was submitted to the Marine Committee "on the illness of the two families at Bidston Telegraph and Lighthouse, in consequence of the paint" suggesting that the work be postponed until the families were better. It was resolved that "the painting would not be proceeded with at present."[24]

The semaphore system, like the flag system before it, certainly had limitations in that it could not be used at night or if visibility was reduced by fog or rain, so the advent of electricity in the mid-nineteenth century was obviously a step forward. The first electric cable was laid from Holyhead to Great Orme in August 1859, and by 5th October it had reached Voel Nant.

During a severe storm on 25th/26th October the iron ship Royal Charter, bound from Melbourne to Liverpool, was wrecked in Moelfre Bay, Anglesey.[25] It is sad to reflect that this ship, carrying, among its 400 passengers, many adventurers bringing home their gains from the Australian gold mines, had travelled so far around the world, only to be lost so close to her destination. The resulting enquiry advised that the Meteorological Department of the Board of Trade (the future Meteorological Office) should use the new electric telegraph to warn of imminent storms. On this particular occasion part of the electric cable was itself damaged, so it might not have been a great help. However the first official gale warnings were to follow. They commenced in June 1860.

A few months later the electric cable had reached Hilbre, and was probably installed at Bidston soon afterwards.

The final semaphore message across the whole range of stations from Holyhead to Liverpool was probably sent in late 1860, when there were still a few of the old flagpoles to be seen on Bidston Hill, whereas the Admiralty semaphore systems had finished by the end of 1847.

Throughout most of the semaphore era, Thomas and Jane Nichols may have been the telegraph keepers at Bidston. Parish records show that Thomas Nichols was in residence, in one of the lighthouse cottages, in 1837, and was still there in 1860. Jane Nichols was officially appointed in November 1840 at a salary of £75 per annum. She was also granted £20 to cover "medical attendance rendered necessary by too great exertion in the performance of her duty", apparently brought about by the inconvenient layout of the Telegraph room. Thomas and Jane were assisted by William Morgan (1843 -1853), John Lockley (1853 -1855) and by their daughter, Mary Ann Nichols, from 1855.

William Morgan appears to be the same William Morgan who had been servant to Ann Urmson, the Lighthouse keeper, in 1841, when he was aged 18. About 1851 Thomas and Jane Nichols asked the Marine Committee for an assistant, and the 1851 census shows that William Morgan, now 28, was resident with the Nichols family as servant and assistant telegraph keeper. However, just after Christmas 1852, Thomas Nichols reported that William Morgan had "absented himself from duty" and he "believed he would not return." A lightshipman was sent over as a temporary measure, and William Lord asked, "Is there not some boy in the neighbourhood suitable for the situation?" Two weeks later William Morgan was dismissed and John Lockley, aged 17, was appointed in his place.

By 1861 the Nichols family were no longer on the scene and Charles Johnson had been appointed as Keeper of the Telegraph at Bidston. He was assisted by Edward Irving, aged 17, who was later replaced by John Shaw aged 15. Charles Johnson did not remain in the post of Keeper for very long. In September 1861 he was replaced by James Adams, who had been moved from the station on Puffin Island with an allowance of 40/- for removal expenses. James Adams had first requested a transfer to a mainland station back in 1847, but he seems to have waited 14 years for this to happen. The following year John Shaw moved over to Albert Dock as a messenger boy, and James Adams' daughter Mary replaced him at a wage of 8/- per week.[26]

When the Bidston Telegraph Station and Lighthouse were amalgamated in 1869 (see Lighthouse Chapter) James Adams was appointed Keeper, with John Urmson as principal assistant and Mary Adams as junior assistant on a wage of 12/- per week. A few months later Mary Adams resigned and her sister Jane Adams aged 18 took her place.

The Marine Committee ordered the removal of the semaphore masts from Bidston in 1862 but it was 1864 before this actually happened.

Chapter Four

Waterloo Dock Observatory: Bidston's Precursor

Waterloo Dock Observatory (Courtesy National Museums Liverpool)

The first suggestion that there should be an astronometrical observatory in Liverpool was made in 1765. On 1st May it was ordered, on the advice of William Everard, architect, surveyor and founder of the Liverpool Library, that "the Corporation do give fifty guineas towards the building and furnishing an observatory in this town."[1]

Land was purchased from Rev. Mr. Maddock, Rector of Liverpool and building began in a field near St. Peter le Poer, on the future Hope Street, possibly on the site of the present Philharmonic Hall, as this is the highest point of Hope Street. Everard designed the building and contributed additional finance from his own funds. Several leading Liverpool merchants agreed to contribute financially, but not all the promised money materialized. The supply of money ran out, several lawsuits followed, building was abandoned and eventually the structure was allowed to fall into ruin.

A report from 1773 states: "The Observatory is a small building, erected upon a pleasing elevation on the east side of the town. It was intended to encourage the study of Astronomy, by affording a convenient place and a proper apparatus for astronomical observations; and the care and direction of the affair was to have been committed to some person capable of giving instruction and assistance to young navigators and astronomers. A design which, well executed, must have been of important advantage to a commercial town. But through some strange neglect of mismanagement, the design had failed: and the building is left unfinished, and will probably soon be in ruins."[2]

Ebenezer Henderson planned to build an Observatory on the roof of the New Mechanics Building, but because of a fire at that building on March 30th 1837, he applied for an alternative site on St. James' Mount, not very far from Everard's site. Henderson had great plans for this small, probably privately owned, building, which enjoyed panoramic views over to North Wales. However nothing more is known about it. Perhaps it was eclipsed by the proposal for a more substantial Observatory which Liverpool Town Council now had under consideration. Henderson's observatory is marked on an

Ordnance Survey map published in 1849, but the site is now buried somewhere among the foundations of the Liverpool Anglican Cathedral.

Meanwhile, in 1834, Lieutenant Jones, R.N. had written to the "Common Council" about his concern that the longitude of Liverpool was unknown and consequently Greenwich Time could not be calculated here. Very accurate time was known only at Greenwich, and at a few other centres such as Oxford and Cambridge, which had their own established observatories. Accurate time could be calculated only by using observation of the stars as they passed overhead. Of course local noon at Liverpool occurred as the sun passed directly overhead, but this was not accurate enough for navigation. It was known that the earth rotates through 15° in one hour, but as it was not known at that time just how many degrees west of Greenwich Liverpool actually was, the exact time difference between the two 'noons' could not be calculated. As, hitherto, the fastest communication between London and Liverpool had been on horseback, a journey of several days, even a pocket watch, most carefully set to Greenwich time before starting on the journey to Liverpool, would not give a very reliable comparison when subsequently compared with Liverpool local time. Now that railway trains were coming on the scene, faster travel meant that the time differences between towns were becoming much more apparent. As Adrian Jarvis points out "the fastest E-W trains of 1840 were already 'faster' travelling West to East than East to West."[4] A pocket watch would now arrive giving a better indication of Greenwich Time, but even so it would be too inaccurate for navigation at sea.

Two years later, as nothing had happened in the meantime, Lieutenant Jones wrote again to the Council. Drawing on his experience of more than a quarter of a century in charge of His Majesty's Ships with chronometers (ships' clocks) under his care, Lieutenant Jones spoke of the importance of an observatory for giving accurate time: an error of only one second per day in the working of a chronometer would, after a two month voyage, result in an error in longitude of fifteen miles, one third of the distance between the Irish and Welsh coasts at the entrance of St. Georges Channel.

Masters of ships in the Thames had the advantage of observing the time ball at Greenwich, which could be seen from the Principal Docks, while observers at Spithead could see the time ball on the Naval College at Portsmouth. He added, "Of the various improvements now in progress or in contemplation by the Corporation, there is not one in my opinion of so much importance to the Foreign Commerce of the town, as that of erecting an Observatory for the rating of ships' chronometers; particularly since the India trade has been thrown open." [5]

The letter was considered by an Improvement Committee, which resolved that "this Committee agrees in opinion with Lieutenant Jones as to the expediency of such an erection, but that under present circumstances the further consideration of the subject be postponed." (Shortage of funds?)

Two months later William Lassell, a well-known local astronomer, wrote to Liverpool Town Council, using the following words : "But it appears to me that in this most extensive and increasing sea port, the ascertaining and publishing officially, true mean Liverpool Time in such a manner as to afford to Mariners and others the means of determining with all attainable accuracy the errors of chronometers and other time-pieces, would of itself be an object of sufficient importance, and yet would involve comparatively only a very trivial expense."[6] He suggested that an observatory be built, which would feature a time ball, a room "20 feet by 15 for the principal instruments, and a smaller ante-room for books, calculations, etc.", plus an observatory dome and sliding door "so that all the sky may be successively exposed." He estimated the total price for all the instrumentation would be £168. This letter was read to the fourth quarterly meeting of the Council on August 3rd 1836, and as a result another Improvement Committee was appointed to consider the matter.

Another year passed before, in 1837, William Lassell and Lieutenant Jones were backed up by the British Association for the Advancement of Science which was meeting in Liverpool that September. The Association "memorialized" the Council about the need for "time and tide" observations to be made at Liverpool. The memorial also pointed out the need for research into the magnetic effect on chronometers of iron hulled ships.[7] The Council decided to set up a conference with the Dock Committee, and in March 1838 it was decided to approve the setting up of an Observatory. A generous £5000 was approved for the cost of erection and £500 for annual outlay, the costs to be shared equally between the Council and the Dock Committee.

However the Dock Committee subsequently withdrew from the agreement saying that "Upon reconsideration this

Committee is of the opinion they would not be justified in contributing ANY sum from the funds of this Trust towards the erection or support of an Observatory."

Seven months later the Liverpool Literary and Philosophical Society memorialized the Council "praying" it to establish an Observatory and to apply to the Lords of the Treasury or to Parliament for leave to "apply a portion of the upper Flat and Western end of the Customhouse to that purpose."[8] Yet another committee was set up. It recommended a go-ahead saying that it had reason to believe that the expenses of erecting, fitting and maintaining an Observatory for practical maritime purposes would be very much less than previous computations had suggested. They asked Mr. Jesse Hartley, Surveyor of the Docks, and Captain H. M. Denham, R.N., Marine Surveyor to the Port, for their opinions about the site.

Captain Denham suggested that the old Custom-house, which already boasted a dome, be converted into an observatory, and he enthusiastically set out in detail his plans for the alterations.

He even added a specification and estimate of cost:-

Initial outlay: - Conversion, Instruments and Equipment - £700

Running costs: - One Astronomer, one Assistant, one Messenger and Office Cleaner, together with books, stationery, coals and candles - £770 per annum.

Captain Denman's frustration can only be guessed at, for at the end of his report on the subject he wrote just two words (in large print) - NO REPLY![9]

The Observatory Committee minute book throws some light on this matter. Captain Denham's proposals were considered, but concern was expressed that the Custom-house might be subject to tremor which would affect the telescope readings. The Committee Chairman was asked to write to Captain Denham asking him to carry out further tests. However the letter was not sent because in the interim there had been "a cessation of this connection with the Dock Trust."[10] No explanation was given.

However, the "memorial" was successful to the extent that the Town Council at last gave the go-ahead to build an observatory elsewhere in the town. On the recommendation of Mr. Richard Adie, a respected Liverpool instrument maker and optician, Jesse Hartley's plan for a site at the recently constructed Waterloo Dock close to the river wall, directly across the river from Seacombe Ferry, was approved. Here there already existed a circular building "brought up from the rock" which was sufficiently large for the purpose.

The Dock Committee agreed to the plans, but made the following stipulation: "The buildings to be allowed to remain so long as they are used for the purposes of an Observatory and that they are not found to interfere with any future improvement or alteration of the Dock or the Quay. This committee reserving to itself the right of removal upon proper notice being given and requiring a rent of twenty shillings per annum for the use of the site."[11]

In 1841 the Observatory Committee suggested that a navigation school for the instruction of "Masters and Mates" be attached to the Western side of the Observatory.[12] This would be of great value to the port and the means of yielding income to lighten the expense.

Work on the Liverpool Observatory duly commenced and was completed in 1844, although even after it opened there was some controversy.

In 1845 there was lengthy correspondence in the Liverpool Times and in the Mercury between Rev. Sheepshanks, an amateur astronomer from Cambridge, and a Mr. John Taylor. Mr.Taylor felt that the Waterloo Dock Observatory was too small, too close to the river and too low-lying. It would suffer from salt spray and from pollution from a nearby alkali works, and its views would be limited by Everton Brow and Bidston Hill. He was also concerned that the impact of waves in the river might upset the Equatorial telescope. Rev. Sheepshanks, for his part, felt the observatory was more than adequate. He had powerful academic friends, so his arguments appear to have won the day. The worries about wave impact on the telescope proved unjustified - the massive stone base was sound and there were no such problems.[13]

The building comprised a room for the testing of chronometers, a transit room, an equatorial room (with a dome) and a "computing" room, together with a dwelling house for the astronomer and his family. The chronometer and transit rooms were on the second floor, accessible either directly from the dwelling house or from the equatorial room. The dwelling house had a flat roof enabling the astronomer to have an uninterrupted view. Stone fronts were built on to the principal elevations of the Observatory. The navigation school was actually built on the eastern side, and the dwelling house faced the river. Total cost of the erection was £2050.

On the recommendation of William Lassell, John Hartnup (see Chapter Fourteen) was appointed as the resident director (resident because many astronomical observations were of necessity made during the hours of darkness). His salary, £200 per annum, was paid from 20th December 1843.

The purposes of the Observatory were set out by the 'Docks and Harbour Board' as:-

a) To determine the exact longitude of Liverpool.

b) To give accurate time to the port of Liverpool by observing stars with a transit telescope and the dropping of a signal ball at 1pm.

c) To test and rate ships' chronometers.

d) To undertake continuous meteorological observations.[14]

In order to fulfil these requirements the finest available instruments were obtained. Apart from the Transit and Equatorial telescopes (see Chapter Sixteen), the other instruments installed included a sidereal clock (which would be used to keep time according to the stars rather than the sun) on which local time could be set, and a mean time clock to show Greenwich Time.

Following a series of observations the latitude and longitude of the Waterloo Dock Observatory were calculated to be 53° 24' 48'' N. and 3° 0' 1'' W. The Astronomer Royal, Sir George Biddell Airy, wished to determine the difference in longitude between Greenwich and Valentia in Ireland, and decided to use Liverpool as an intermediate station.

John Hartnup was elected to the Royal Astronomical Society (R. A. S.) in February 1845.

Mr. Hartnup was instructed to drop a time ball each day except Sunday (the one at the Royal Observatory, Greenwich had already been in use for about 20 years), so that people in the city could set their timepieces by it. The 'ball', a large wicker sphere, was hoisted up a mast on the roof of the observatory, and at precisely 1 p.m. each day it was allowed to fall.[15]

An advertisement placed by "John Hartnup, Observer", in the Liverpool Times on 28th January 1845, states:-

"Masters of Ships and the Public generally are informed that the signal ball on the top of the Observatory recently erected on Waterloo Dock Pier Head, is dropped daily at One o'clock Greenwich Mean Time, being Twelve Minutes and Two-tenths of a Second before One o'clock at this Observatory.

Chronometers are received and rated at the Observatory, at the charge of 7s.6d. each. The system of rating adopted is precisely the same as that pursued at Greenwich by the Astronomer Royal.

The respective Owners will be furnished with the gain or loss of their Chronometers for each day, and the temperature of the room in which the Chronometers are placed, in addition to the error on Greenwich Time, and the mean daily rate. By order of the Observatory Committee of the Town Council."

Thus began the rating of chronometers - marine clocks based on the Eighteenth Century inventions of John Harrison, which are so ably described in Dava Sobel's book "Longitude." Aboard ship these were balanced on gimbals to keep them horizontal even in the roughest seas.

The owner or captain of any ship for which dock rates had been paid in Liverpool was permitted to send his chronometers to the Observatory for testing.

Mr. Hartnup met with some opposition from the local chronometer and watchmakers, who felt that activities at the new Observatory were treading on their toes. They requested that the Observatory be conducted on the same principles as Greenwich "where chronometers were neither sold nor rated except for Government." At an Observatory Committee meeting in 1844, one member, Mr. Birkett, remarked that "he had no idea of the establishment doing a retail business and interfering with tradesmen."

A particularly aerated letter from an anonymous chronometer maker was sent to the Liverpool Mercury in 1847. The writer took offence at a letter from the Astronomer Royal, which seemed to be saying "Come to our shop (the Observatory), we can serve you better than any private establishment."

Mr. Hartnup believed that temperature variation at different latitudes affected chronometers more than any other factor. Ships' clocks tended to run too slowly in cold latitudes, their lubricating oils having thickened up, and too fast in tropical regions as the oil thinned down. So if, for example, a ship sailed to Liverpool from the Pacific via Cape Horn, its chronometer might well slow down round the Cape and gain as it headed up the Atlantic across the Equator. A few minutes' error in the clock could send the ship disastrously off course. Thus John Hartnup wished to monitor chronometers over a range of temperatures.

The architect who originally designed the Observatory had not made any provision for controlling the temperature in the chronometer room. Scientists at the Royal Observatory, Greenwich, had assured him that this was not necessary, as marine timekeepers were always compensated for temperature change. John Hartnup was not happy about this.[16] He found that the chronometer room temperature could vary by as much as 20° F. in winter and 30° F. in summer.

For instance, in the summer of 1844 the chronometers of several American packet ships had been brought to the Observatory for the purpose of rating. The rates of the instruments, while on test in an average temperature of 60" F., compared well with the rates noted on the Atlantic crossings. However, the following winter the same chronometers were returned for rating. The temperature of the chronometer room now ranged between 40°F and 50° F. The compared rates now gave an error in ship's longitude of 1 degree or 60 nautical miles on the Equator on a voyage lasting 15 - 20 days - a potentially disastrous error. When the chronometers were moved to a warmer room the original rates returned.[17]

To counteract the problem John Hartnup set up a gas-fired "hotbox", which could house a number of chronometers, and the temperature could be varied after a few days.

Each chronometer test lasted three months. The ship's captain could then be presented with a table of corrections to be applied to the chronometer as the vessel passed through various latitudes during the voyage. A typical table follows:

At 47° Fahrenheit the chronometer loses 6.5 seconds per day.
At 60° Fahrenheit the chronometer loses 7.3 seconds per day.
At 65° Fahrenheit the chronometer loses 7.9 seconds per day.
At 70° Fahrenheit the chronometer loses 8.9 seconds per day.
At 75° Fahrenheit the chronometer loses 9.9 seconds per day.

At 80°Fahrenheit the chronometer loses 10.9 seconds per day.
At 85° Fahrenheit the chronometer loses 12.3 seconds per day.
At 90° Fahrenheit the chronometer loses 13.9 seconds per day.[18]

So if, for example, the vessel were sailing through the Tropics, and the thermometer was reading 80° F, the captain would know he should adjust his chronometer by 10.9 seconds each day to improve its accuracy. The above figures were taken from original ledgers, written in copperplate handwriting by Hartnup himself, and now in the care of The World Museum. It is interesting to note that the above table refers to a chronometer which apparently went faster at lower temperatures. John Hartnup noted that "Some chronometers go faster in cold than in heat, others go faster in heat than in cold, while some have nearly the same rate in 55° and 85°." He also noted that often chronometers had "a tendency to gain on the rate when new." Thus it was desirable that every chronometer should have its own table of corrections.

In September 1847 he was instructed to appoint a suitable person to assist in the reception and delivery of chronometers. The man appointed was John Shearer. His salary was £80 per annum.

The Astronomer Royal was so impressed with Mr. Hartnup's system that in 1850 he asked to be supplied with drawings of the heating apparatus used for testing chronometers at the Waterloo Dock Observatory with a view to installing a similar system at Greenwich for the testing of naval chronometers. A few years later he reported that "a chronometer oven" had been provided (at Greenwich) copied from that of

Liverpool Observatory, and the following year he reported that the oven had been in "perpetual" use. To quote him: "I anticipate considerable benefit, not only to the Royal Navy, but also to habits of chronometer makers, from thus regularly directing our attention to the important thermal adjustments". He acknowledged that "the careful attention to the subject of temperature is in no small degree due to the example set by Mr. Hartnup at the Liverpool Observatory." The apparatus was adopted for use by at least two Liverpool chronometer makers, Mr. Hornby and another, perhaps Mr. Roskell. Professor William Cranch Bond of the U.S.A. (see below) subsequently installed the system in Boston.

By August 1851 John Hartnup was showing signs of mild exasperation with the local clock manufacturers: "The signal ball has been dropped daily at one o'clock Greenwich mean time. Notwithstanding that the time is published in this way daily, there are a great many applications made at the Observatory for Greenwich Time, chiefly by professional raters of chronometers, who either miss the time for observing the ball, or have not confidence in their own observations. We have never refused to give the time when applied to in this way, but as the duties of the Observatory have of late much increased, we have, when applications have been very frequent by the same persons, requested that they would learn to observe the drop of the ball, and this request has been generally complied with."

The problem was partially resolved the following year, for by this time electric power was becoming available and time balls could be erected at a distance from observatories, connected by cable, and operated by a remote switch. Mr. Hartnup reported that a time ball was erected above Charing Cross Bridge in London, but was operated from Greenwich and dropped simultaneously with the one at the Royal Observatory, so that it would be visible to a greater area of London and to vessels passing "below the bridge." A time ball was duly set up at the Victoria Tower in Liverpool, its control clock being connected to the Waterloo Dock by landline.

The Equatorial telescope was used to observe planets and comets (see Chapter Sixteen).

In 1849, under the auspices of the United States Coast Survey, the Liverpool Observatory started a project in conjunction with Professor William Cranch Bond of Cambridge University, Boston, Massachusetts, to determine the exact longitude of the Cambridge Observatory. Steam-powered mail packet ships were now crossing the Atlantic on a regular basis, so the opportunity arose to take chronometer readings at Liverpool and then transport the chronometers across to Boston to take readings there. No expense was spared by the U.S. authorities. The trials were repeated three times and a stateroom was reserved on each voyage to house the chronometers and their keeper, Sydney Coolidge, who, with his assistant, wound them up and took careful readings of temperature, barometric pressure and inclination of the vessel at specified times. In all, 175 chronometers were tested at Liverpool, taken across the Atlantic by steamship, and read at Cambridge. The final mean of all the readings gave a longitude considered to be not more than one second in error, which would equate to a distance of about one nautical mile.[19]

In 1849 John Hartnup had designed an improved form of compensation balance for chronometers, with the aim of reducing the time errors caused by temperature variation. William Shepherd, a Liverpool chronometer maker, tested the new balance in one of his instruments. He found that the temperature induced errors were virtually eliminated. Several of the city instrument makers agreed to incorporate this balance into their chronometers. (They had by now recognised the value of the observatory and were consulting Mr. Hartnup). Five of Mr. Shepherd's instruments were among those used in the Cambridge (Massachusetts) - Liverpool exercise, and Professor Bond reported that those particular chronometers did indeed show the least variation with temperature.

John Hartnup refused to patent his balance and made no secret of its construction. Instead he made it freely available to the chronometer trade and published its description widely.[20] However, his balance was not nearly as strong as the standard balances currently in use at that time, making it more susceptible to damage. It was larger and more difficult to make and to adjust, so presumably it would have been a lot more expensive than ordinary balances.

The United States exercise lasted almost six years, but was not without its problems. Alexander Bache, the superintendent of the U.S. Coast Survey, a scientist noted for his uncompromising attention to precise measurements, wanted to supervise John Hartnup's observation programme at Liverpool, and indicated his wishes via Professor Bond. John Hartnup refused to be dictated to in this way. As a result Bache wanted Professor Bond to abandon Liverpool, but the

Professor had great faith in John Hartnup's methods and refused to comply. Bache had to accept defeat. In recognition of Liverpool's contribution, Professor Bond presented the Observatory with a very handsome and accurate sidereal clock, which became known as the Bond Clock (see photo) and which was to take pride of place in the Waterloo Dock Observatory and the future Bidston Observatory for many years to come. It is now in the care of The World Museum, Liverpool.

The Bond Clock (Courtesy National Museums Liverpool)

By December 1851 John Hartnup felt that he was due for a salary increase. He pointed out that he had not had an increase in the eight years since his appointment and in the interim he had turned down offers of "calculation and teaching" which would have been of benefit. His salary was duly raised from £200 to £300 per annum. His assistant, John Shearer, also took the opportunity to ask for a rise, and his wages were increased from £80 to £100 per annum.

The R.A.S. was very complimentary about the Liverpool Observatory and its Astronomer in the annual report of 1852. It noted that: "Chronometers are tested at the (Liverpool) Observatory with better means than any other establishment, except Greenwich, enjoys. We should be glad to learn that other ports had followed, even a long way off, the example of Liverpool, and enabled the seaman to prove the goodness of his chronometers and to learn their errors and rates with scrupulous exactness.

Of the Liverpool Observatory nothing new need be said. It maintains its reputation as the most trustworthy for extra - meridianal observations for immediate use. The excellence of his Equatorial enables Mr. Hartnup to compare all his objects with one or more perfectly well determined stars so that he obtains at once what an observer less completely equipped (i.e. almost every other observer) may wait months to obtain." [21]

The British Association held a meeting in Liverpool in 1854. Professor Phillips paid a glowing tribute to the Waterloo Dock Observatory. He said, "It was at the Liverpool meeting of the Association in 1837 that the establishment of an Observatory was proposed; and now, on our return to Liverpool, we find the Observatory completed and working well, producing results which, it is not too much to say, cannot be produced at any other Observatory in the world, and which results are at this moment of the highest possible importance in correcting many of our views in regard to the conditions of the atmosphere. Certainly at this moment there is no Observatory more important than this: none from which can be obtained such practically useful and accurate results."

In 1854, when photography was in its infancy, the British Association offered a prize for the best photograph of the moon. Professor Bond had obtained good results in America using a Daguerreotype silver-plate process, and the British Association was keen to match his achievement. The Liverpool Photographic Society, in the person of Mr. J. A. Forrest, approached John Hartnup, who agreed to photograph the moon using the Equatorial telescope at Waterloo Dock. The time taken to photograph the moon varied between thirty seconds and three minutes, and it required a very steady hand on the part of Mr. Hartnup to produce a sharp focus. Eventually this was achieved, but the resulting photo measured only one and one third inches in diameter. Mr. Forrest and Mr. Hartnup borrowed a magic lantern, and were amazed to find that an image thrown onto a screen of 25 feet diameter was almost as sharp as the original. It was proposed to project the image onto a 56 feet square screen on the side of St. George's Hall. Describing the experiment in a paper presented to the HSLC (Historical Society of Lancashire and Cheshire) in 1863, Mr. Forrest said, "In the course of our experiments a question arose as to the practicality of taking a stereoscopic view of the moon. Mr. Hartnup suggested a plan by which this would be settled: it was by taking the moon twelve hours before her full and then twelve hours after, and the result was that we got a shadow of both sides. We put these impressions into the stereoscope, on looking through which, the moon appeared a perfect ball." [22]

The resulting photographs were displayed in an exhibition "around the country."

In 1855 using the idea of remote control Mr. Hartnup arranged with the Magnetic Telegraph Company for a telegraph line to be laid between the Observatory and their office in Exchange Buildings. A Henley Electromagnetic clock was placed in the office window, having "a beautiful large dial with hour, minute and second hands, which may well be seen from the adjoining Exchange Flags." It was noted on one occasion that "between the hours of 6 a.m. and 5 p.m. 1,860 persons took the time from the clock of the Magnetic Telegraph Company."

In 1857 the Liverpool Town Hall clock was fitted with an electrically controlled remote regulator which kept its pendulum synchronised with the master pendulum at the Observatory. According to John Hartnup, this was "The first large public clock to which this beautiful invention has been applied."

In the same year John Hartnup provided details of the Waterloo Dock Observatory and its instruments to the Committee of Merchants in New York, who were planning to set up an observatory there.

In December 1857 Queen Victoria wished to buy a marine chronometer of "the highest character of performance" for one of her sons, Prince Alfred, perhaps as a Christmas present. Inquiries were made, and the Prince Consort, Albert, was put in touch with the Liverpool Observatory. Fifty-five new chronometers, by various makers, were being tested at the Observatory at the time, prior to being sold to merchant captains and shipowners. One of these instruments was selected and purchased, although there is no indication that Prince Albert visited the Observatory in person to make the selection.

Responsibility for the Observatory was transferred from Liverpool Council to the Marine Committee of the Mersey Docks and Harbour Board in 1858.

In 1859 a clock was installed in the Victoria Tower, Liverpool, at the entrance to Salisbury Dock. It had a dial, eight feet in diameter, on each of the six faces of the tower, and was controlled by landline from the Waterloo Dock Observatory. On a still day its striking could be heard from the Observatory thus allowing for further checks to be made on the clock's accuracy.

By 1861 two time balls were being dropped each day, one at the Observatory and one on top of the Victoria Tower, and three public clocks, at Exchange Buildings, the Town Hall, and the Victoria Tower, were being controlled by line from Waterloo Dock. The Marine Committee recommended that the clocks should be placed under the management of John Hartnup at an estimated additional cost of £24 per annum. George Hardman was duly appointed as Hartnup's second assistant, at a salary of £70 a year, and he was in charge of the timeballs and the winding of clocks.[23]

The following year John Hartnup requested that the service of his son, John Hartnup Junior, might be "continued to him." His son was duly appointed as Assistant Astronomer at a salary of £200 per annum.

Mr. Hartnup was unhappy with the limited facilities for chronometer testing at Waterloo Dock. He had sufficient space to test only a few chronometers at any one time, whereas

Greenwich had the capacity to test many naval instruments. In the early 1860s the Dock Board agreed to a new chronometer room being created at Liverpool. Whether this involved extensions to the building, or merely re-allocation of the existing space is not clear, but the new room was 28 ft by 18 ft with a large double sky-light. The side walls were double with a cavity, and the room was warmed by hot water pipes under the floor. Heating was all by gas pressure, regulated by a governor. At Hartnup's request two warm air chambers were built into the room, each having the capability of housing more than a hundred chronometers. The tops of the chambers were made of plate glass, so that the instruments in their boxes with lids open might be compared frequently and rates at different temperatures could be ascertained.

It must have been frustrating for Mr. Hartnup to discover, soon after these improvements were made, that plans were already afoot to pull down the Observatory within two years in order to develop the Waterloo dock system, thus complying with the Dock Committee's stipulation laid down in 1839.

The proposed re-siting of the Observatory caused protest amongst the businessmen of Liverpool. A memorial sent to the Chairman of the Mersey Docks and Harbour Board in 1864 was signed by more than twenty people. They had been informed that "it was proposed to move the Observatory, and in its stead erect a dwelling house and offices for a dock master." Amongst other benefits of the present location, they cited the long establishment, nearly twenty years, the skilled astronomer's work recorded in so many publications both in Europe and America, and the great outlay of money. They expressed the opinion that "nothing short of grave necessity should decide the question of the removal of an Institution of which Liverpool might feel justly proud." If the proposed dock alteration could not be cancelled, they "begged leave to suggest that the astronomer be instructed to search for a suitable site on the Lancashire side of the River Mersey, that would be at once accessible and sufficiently isolated and elevated."

Chapter Five

Bidston: The Hartnup Era

John Hartnup (Courtesy Proudman Oceanographic Laboratory)

The Mersey Docks and Harbour Board concluded that extensive alterations to Waterloo Dock were indeed desirable, in order to make room for "lofty, vaulted" corn warehouses, and a new site had to be found for the Observatory.[1]

The pleas of the Liverpool businessmen fell on deaf ears, for no suitable place was found on the Liverpool side of the river. However, it was felt that the area of the lighthouse on Bidston

Hill, on the other side of the river, but only three miles from the old site as the crow flies, would make an ideal situation, particularly as it had already been a prominent landmark for more than a century.

About one statute acre of land on Bidston Hill was purchased from Mr.Vyner, who agreed to the removal of restrictions in the conveyancing of the land. Otherwise the building of an Observatory would not have been permitted.

Building commenced in 1864, and the Observatory was constructed of blocks of Triassic Keuper sandstone, (now known as Helsby sandstone), excavated from the site, faced with rusticated ashlar, and topped with a slate roof.

The architect was George Fosbery Lyster. He was the son of an army colonel, and had learnt engineering on the Shannon. He was subsequently appointed engineer-in-chief to the Mersey Docks and Harbour Board, and was responsible for much of the construction and enlargement of the Mersey Docks in the period 1861-1897. On the Wirral side of the river he constructed Alfred Dock and Morpeth Dock and completed Woodside Landing Stage, while on the Liverpool side he designed, among others, Herculaneum Dock, Brocklebank Dock, Langton Dock and Alexandra Dock.[2]

The following diagrams are based on Lyster's very detailed plans of the Observatory, which included designs for the tiled floors, the plaster cornices, and minute details of the domes, doors, etc.

The scale of the original plans (one inch = 10 feet) shows that the building is 90 feet long by 76 feet wide, and covers an area of 760 square yards.

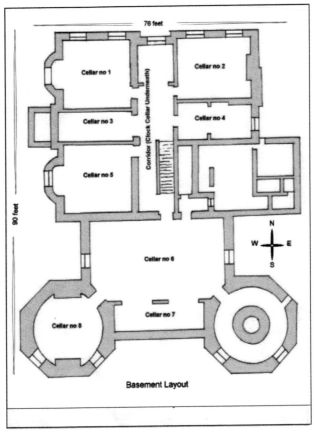

Basement Layout

Cellars 12 feet deep were constructed below ground, and beneath these was a sub-basement cellar 12 feet deep and 9 feet wide extending N - S through the centre of the building. This was known as the clock cellar. It was constructed in the solid rock to reduce the variation in temperature, and as a result the range between mid-summer and mid-winter was less than 1° Centigrade. This provided ideal conditions for the testing of chronometers.

The instrument room was 36 feet long and 21 feet wide. It contained two warm air chambers heated by gas from the cellar below, each designed to hold 100 chronometers so arranged that they could be compared with the normal clock (reading G.M.T.) without being moved. The sidereal clock and the chronograph were placed in the room above the chronometer room, while sextants, barometers and thermometers were tested in the basement cellar below the Equatorial dome.

Another sub-cellar was dug out of the rock in later years, for use as a boiler room. It is accessed via steps in the northwest corner of cellar number five, and was in recent years (certainly since 1960) used for archive storage.

The living accommodation was generous and occupied more than half the rooms on the north side of the Observatory. In fact the building was referred to on one occasion as "a very good house with an observatory attached." There were (and still are) three entrances. The main entrance is on the south side facing the windmill, and a driveway encircles the building.

Originally, horse-drawn carriages would have reigned in at the front door to allow passengers to dismount. The carriages then continued round the building and down the hill to the stables. The entrance to the living accommodation was on the western side of the building, and had a stout porch added on to give protection against the prevailing westerly winds.

The third entrance faces east, and gives access to the building via the small courtyard and the kitchen.

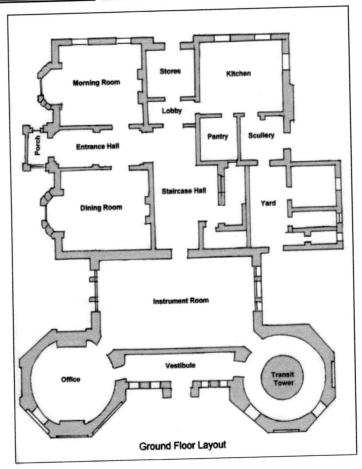

Ground Floor Layout

A deep trench, known as the moat, surrounded the whole building to insulate the telescopes from the vibration caused by the movement of traffic round the building. I well recall that in later years the periodic cleaning out of this trench was one of the less popular activities of the handymen.

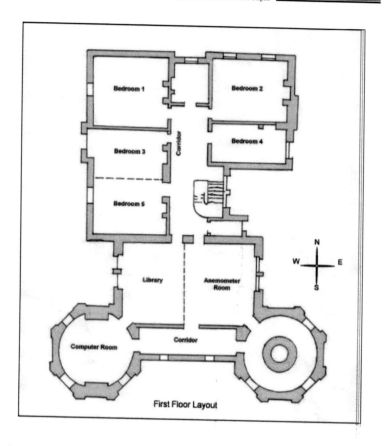

First Floor Layout

On August 11th 1866 the Birkenhead Advertiser reported that "work was drawing towards completion", and that stone from the site had also been supplied to the corn warehouses at Birkenhead and to "other constructions" on the dock estate.

On November 10th the press reported that the Observatory was "all but finished."

The photo shows the portion of the building devoted to living accommodation in the 19th Century.

During the two years of construction John Hartnup made preparations for determining the difference in longitude between the old and new observatories, thus ensuring that accurate time could be recorded at the new site. To ensure continuity of transit checks on longitude, a set of sixty chronometers were set to G.M.T. by observation of star transits at Waterloo Dock. They were then transported to Bidston, and their errors ascertained on the meridian of the new Observatory. All this activity took place in the course of one clear day in mid-winter.

Noon at Bidston Observatory was calculated to occur 17.04 seconds later than that at Waterloo Dock. Noon at the latter was known to be 12 minutes 0.11 seconds later than at Greenwich. Therefore noon at the new site was 12 minutes 17.15 seconds later than at Greenwich (or 3° 4 minutes 17 seconds in arc).

At the same time John Hartnup set up a weather station at Bidston, and temperatures were recorded at both sites over a two-year period prior to the opening of the new Observatory. The results revealed that Bidston was subject to a much larger daily range of temperature than Waterloo Dock. This is reasonable given the fact that the new Observatory did not enjoy the moderating influence of a river flowing only feet away. The overall mean temperature was lower at Bidston. The fact that Bidston was sited 200 feet above sea level would account for this. The original temperature records, carefully handwritten in copperplate, are still in existence in the Proudman Oceanographic Laboratory (POL) archives.

The new Observatory had two domes, the eastern one to house the transit telescope which would continue to observe the passage of stars across the meridian, thus giving accurate time checks, and the western one to house the equatorial telescope, which would continue to observe comets. The equatorial was also used to determine the diameter of the planets Neptune, Saturn and Venus.

Each of the towers was 20 feet across, with the domes rising 20 feet above the stonework. The Transit dome was supported by a pillar 12 feet in diameter rising up from a solid rock foundation, and surrounded by a spiral staircase. In this way the dome did not directly touch any floor, thus providing absolute stability for the transit telescope. Sir George Airy, the Astronomer Royal, described the Transit Circle as the most stable telescope in Britain. The Equatorial dome featured a panel which could be retracted to reveal the overhead sky, as had the one at Waterloo Dock. Both domes could (and still can) be rotated through 360°. The best greenheart timber was used for the wood panels.

This card, postmarked 1904, shows the positioning of the domes and the Robinson Anemometer (I have added the printed words).

A similar view photographed in February 2005, shows how the growth of trees has altered the appearance of the site in 100 years. (The exact spot from which the Observatory is viewed in the postcard is inaccessible because of the bushes).

John Hartnup was greatly impressed with the new building. He felt that the site would be very favourable for astronomical, meteorological and magnetic observations, and the deep underground rooms would be ideal for testing instruments under strict temperature control. At that time instruments used by ships of the Royal Navy were sent for testing to various venues: - chronometers to Greenwich, compasses to Woolwich, and barometers, thermometers and sextants to Kew. John Hartnup felt that, for the Mercantile Marine, all these services could be provided under one roof at Bidston Observatory. The Dock Board, on the recommendation of the Marine Committee, spent £400 pounds on providing facilities for testing compasses, barometers and sextants at Bidston.

By December 20th 1866 the Hartnups had taken up residence and Bidston Observatory was in full operation.

It seems that the Shearers and the Hardings also moved across to Wirral. A Marine Committee minute indicates that John Shearer was allowed £5 towards the cost of removal, while in 1869 John Hartnup reported that the necessity of attending to the Dock Estate clocks in Liverpool was interfering with George Harding's duties at the Observatory. The astronomer requested that the heads of the departments where these clocks were located, namely at Victoria Tower, Albert Dock Warehouses, Wapping Dock and the Engineer's Department, should arrange for the clocks to be attended by their own staff. This was agreed.[3]

At the same time John Hartnup pointed out that "changes

consequent on the removal of the Observatory to Bidston and new regulations for testing of chronometers", together with the extra availability of George Harding, meant that he could now dispense with the services of John Shearer. As a result John Shearer was retired on a pension of £40 per year, and appears to have been happy with the arrangement although he was only 52. He may have been suffering from ill-health, for his death was registered in West Derby, Liverpool only three years later. His wife was allowed to receive payment of his pension for a period of two months following his death.

This card, posted in 1909, shows the cannon at Morpeth Dock

One problem resulting from the move across the river was the matter of the daily one o'clock time signal. A time ball erected on the roof at Bidston site would obviously have been difficult to observe from Liverpool, so John Hartnup suggested that a time gun (See Chapter Fifteen) similar to that established at Edinburgh Castle in 1861, be installed at Morpeth Dock on the Birkenhead side of the river. The firing would have the advantage of being not only visible to observers on or near the river, but also audible from the premises of the chronometer makers in the city. They could then rate their newly manufactured clocks themselves, without having to send them across to Bidston.

John Hartnup's wife Elizabeth died on 24th March 1868, at the age of 67 years, leaving her husband and 24 year old son, John. She had known only three years of life at Bidston.

In 1874 the Astronomer requested that a youth be appointed to assist him in certain duties. This was agreed and the youth was taken on at a wage of 10/- per week. The youth in question may well have been Fred Skinner who was then aged 14 and who, twelve years later, appears in the diaries as John Hartnup Junior's senior assistant.

John Hartnup was unhappy about the state of the roadway up the hill. In September 1874 he wrote to Captain G.H.Hills R.N. at the Dock Board:

The old road up the hill in the late nineteenth century. (Courtesy Glyn Holden)

"Dear Sir,
On the Dock Board availing themselves of their right of way to the Observatory and Lighthouse, Mr. Vyner claimed the exclusive right to make that part of the road which passes through his land. This road, which was very imperfectly made at first, has now become so bad that it is not safe for a carriage to be drawn over it. I have been informed that a

valuable horse belonging to Sir Edward Cust has been injured by driving it up here, and the spring of a cab which I took up to the Observatory was broken in passing over that part of the road owned by Mr. Vyner. Will you be good enough to obtain the authority of the Marine Committee to write to Mr. Vyner or his agent on the subject.
Yours truly,
John Hartnup."

In October the Marine Surveyor was directed by the Committee to endeavour to arrange with Mr. Vyner's agent for suitable improvement to the road.
(No more information on the subject is available.)

John Hartnup (Senior) corresponded regularly with the Royal Astronomical Society. One particularly interesting letter reads:
"25 August 1871 Chippenham, Wiltshire (Presumably Hartnup was on holiday at the time.)
Sir,
When (your) deputation is viewing the eclipse in December next it will be a good opportunity to make a very simple experiment which will at once decide the question as to the earth's shape. If the equator or zenith (line) be a direct and straight line, like the seam of a cricket ball, the earth is a globe; if curvilinear it is as I (suspect - or assert) a plane, and a row of ten perpendicular posts underneath the Zenith, of not less than a mile apart, will show no lateral shadow. If the sun's course be a circle, there will be a lateral shadow (......) of them. If you are not afraid of the (.....), let this be tried.
Yours truly"

(The gaps in the letters arose because it is impossible to read John Hartnup's handwriting at times!)

Unfortunately I have been unable to find out if there was any outcome to this suggestion. Maybe it was cloudy during the eclipse in December.

A letter written to the Secretary of the R.A.S. on 17th October 1874 reads -

"Dear Sir,
A few days ago I sent a letter to the R.A.S. which I had received from a son of Dr. Nevins of Liverpool, on the application of corrections due to changes of temperature to the rates of their chronometers during a voyage from Liverpool to Calcutta. Some of our leading ship owners feel an interest in this letter from the circumstances of Mr. Nevins having received his education in Nautical Astronomy on board the "Conway" training ship. Mr. Nevins was an apprentice in the employ of Thos & Jno Brocklebank and having served his time when the ship arrived at Calcutta he left her there and returned to Liverpool. He is now First Officer in an Australian sailing ship. If the Council should think this letter appropriate for the Monthly Notices I would like to have 100 extra copies for distribution amongst the ship owners in Liverpool.
Yours truly
John Hartnup"

Arthur Nevins was familiar with John Hartnup's work, and he noted that the chronometers on board his ship, the Tenasserim, had been issued with certificates of temperature correction at Bidston more that two years earlier. Prior to setting sail from Liverpool the two chronometers were set to G.M.T. using the one o'clock gun signal and to 55° F., the current air temperature. During the voyage to Calcutta readings were taken daily, keeping two tables, one showing direct readings and the other giving adjusted readings in accordance with John Hartnup's correction tables. At the end of the voyage G.M.T. was noted using the Calcutta time gun. It was found that, by applying the temperature corrections issued more than two years earlier, the two chronometers agreed with each other throughout the voyage to within a few seconds. By supposing a uniform 55° F. throughout, however, the time errors were 4 minutes 52 seconds and 1 minute 13 seconds respectively. On return to the Thames after a voyage of eight months, the time errors, allowing for temperature change, were 5 seconds and 1 minute 14 seconds respectively. In terms of actual distance this means that the error in longitude, taking an average of the two chronometers readings, was, when temperature changes were taken into account, about equal to the distance from New Brighton to Rock Ferry (two districts about 4-5 miles apart on Wirral). By ignoring temperature changes, the averaged error was 10 minutes 16 seconds, equal to the distance from Liverpool to Hull. [4]

A letter sent to a ship owner in 1882 reveals something of the method of chronometer testing:-

"Dear Sir,

Our usual method of testing chronometers is for a period of five weeks in three definite temperatures, in the following order: 55°, 70°, 85°, 70° and 55°. The Rates are given for six days in each week."

These memos are taken from a set of eight daybooks covering the years 1882 to the 1920s, containing 'carbon' copies of letters handwritten by the Directors, as well as tables of chronometer corrections calculated for individual ships, notably those belonging to the Pacific Steam Navigation Company, as well as correspondence on weather statistics. Unfortunately the incoming correspondence to which these memos relate has not been preserved.

The books are now in a fragile state, and much of the information is difficult to read. These volumes are in the care of The World Museum, Liverpool.

A stationery list dated July 21st 1882 reads, among other items:-

1/2 ream Foolscap Copying paper   4s-0d
1 pint Copying ink   2s-0d
Postage stamps for the year   £3-15s-6d

In 1883, at the age of 77, John Hartnup began to suffer ill health. In response to a request from the Town Clerk of Preston, he wrote -
"I am not well and do not expect to be able to leave the Observatory for a week or two." He was unfit for work in May and again in September, but after that he was "looking much better" and talking of going to London for a week's holiday.

John Hartnup's son, John Hartnup Junior, was largely responsible for the running of the meteorological station. In a letter to Mr. Nicholas of Wavertree, dated 16th June 1884,

John Hartnup Junior said "In reply to your letter of the 13th inst. I have to say that the lowest temperature recorded at this Observatory since its establishment in 1867 was 8.5 F. on the 25th of January 1881." The reading was confirmed by a similar letter sent to the press office of the 'Courier' by John Hartnup Senior in December 1884. He reported - "In 1881 from January 7th to 26th inclusive the mean temperature was below freezing on each day. During the 24 hours ending at 0900 on the 25th the highest reading of the thermometer was 21.3 F. and the lowest 8.5 F. These are the lowest readings for any one day that have been recorded at this Observatory and the above the longest period of continuous frost."
This very low reading has never been equalled at Bidston.

These were the early days of Meteorological Office (M.O.) coding systems, and Bidston was one of the stations whose daily weather reports were coded up. There were obvious teething troubles, as a letter sent by John Hartnup Junior to The Secretary, Met Office, on 26th August 1885 reveals: -
"In our report for 25th inst. the Met Bulb (air temperature) is printed 44 instead of 54. Our fifth group was sent 54000."
Further printing errors were reported to the Secretary, Met Office, on three more occasions before the end of the year.

Certified weather reports were supplied frequently to clients in the second half of the 19th Century. The following letter sent by John Hartnup in May 1884 reveals the method used in those days:-
"Gentlemen,
Will you be kind enough to apply to the Solicitor of the Mersey Docks and Harbour Board for permission for us to

supply the information which you require. On obtaining this your clerk can make the necessary abstracts from our records which we will certify.

Certified abstracts from the records of this Observatory have been accepted as evidence for many years past in the Admiralty and other law courts."

No charges were made for the reports at that time, but as the years went by charges for weather reports were introduced, possibly by Mr. Plummer, the Hartnups' successor. More than a hundred years later Bidston still provided weather reports, although many statistics can now be picked up from the Internet.

John Hartnup sent his last annual report to the Management Committee of the MDHB in 1883.

As his health continued to fail, he decided to retire in May 1885 at the age of 79, and moved to London to seek medical advice. Despite this he died rather unexpectedly in London on October 20th in the same year.

He had been Director of the Observatories for 42 years.

A glowing tribute to the great improvement in the accuracy of chronometers, resulting from John Hartnup's work, was made by Henry Watt, Vice-President of the Mercantile Marine Service Association in their Reporter magazine in January 1886. He told of how he had been in charge of a ship which sailed in 1885 from New York to Brisbane, then via Torres Strait to Rangoon and Cape Colony, a voyage lasting five months. His ship relied on a chronometer rated at Bidston. As a result of applying John Hartnup's supplied table of time corrections as the air temperature varied, he found, on arrival at Cape Colony, that the chronometer registered an error of only 48 seconds when compared with G.M.T. Without the corrections for temperature it would have been several minutes in error and the ship could have been well off course. He praised John Hartnup's genius, modesty and perseverance.[5]

Another tribute to Hartnup's work appeared in the Report of the Council to the Royal Astronomical Society in February 1886. It referred to "the post which John Hartnup had held for nearly forty-two years with so much credit to himself and advantage to the mercantile marine of the Port of Liverpool."

Chapter Six

Bidston - John Hartnup Junior: Director 1885 - 1892

Following his father's retirement, John Hartnup Junior took over the Directorship of Bidston, and continued to reside at the Observatory.

While his father was still alive he practised the accepted convention of signing himself as John Hartnup Junior. For instance, he started a weather report written in October 1885, with the words - "I, John Hartnup Junior, Director of the Liverpool Observatory, Bidston, Birkenhead, hereby certify ...."

He was by now married to Lucy Hammond from Ashford, Kent, ten years his junior. Lucy's younger sister, Kathleen, lived with them. They had two live-in servants, Eliza Bond, aged 53, a cook-domestic and Emma Houghland, aged 21, a housemaid.

John Hartnup faithfully carried on his father's astronomical work. He continued chronometer testing and wrote several papers on the subject, but declined to take any responsibility for the actual cleaning or repair of chronometers - that was the

job of the makers. A letter written in January 1887 says:-
"The chronometer Penlington and Halton 2104, the property of the Pacific Steam Navigation Company and appropriated to their SS Magella stopped during the last voyage of the vessel. I shall be obliged by your sending to the Observatory for the instrument and having it cleaned and repaired as soon as possible", and another letter, addressed to a local clock maker in 1889, says:-
"Be good enough to send for your chronometer which was left here this afternoon and have the gimbals put right when we will test it (after). It is quite useless to attempt to do this in its present condition."

Chronometers were received and issued at the Observatory between the hours of 10 am and 4 pm (3 pm on Saturdays).

John Hartnup enthusiastically continued the meteorological work, and actively encouraged visitors. Some of those groups noted in the daybooks included the YMCA, the Post and Telegraph Christian Association, the Liverpool Welsh Philosophical Society, the Liverpool Science Students' Association, the Pupil Teachers' College and the Edge Hill Science Club. Many of these parties crossed the river by ferry, and then boarded a tramcar at Woodside. In a letter to the Crewe Scientific Society, who were due to visit the Observatory in July 1885, Hartnup pointed out that "A tram-car runs every ten minutes from Woodside Ferry to the Dock Station up the Hoylake railway, which is about a quarter hour's walk from the Observatory."
However John Hartnup stipulated that no visiting group should exceed ten persons, because of "possible injury to

instruments and also because they (the instruments) cannot be satisfactorily explained under such circumstances." In March 1886 he assured Mr. I. Weir of Princes Road, Liverpool that he would have "much pleasure in showing the members of the University astronomical class the Observatory at 4 pm on Saturday the 27th inst. and if the weather permits to afford them an opportunity of looking at the planet Saturn at 7 pm on that evening." The group also wished to visit the lighthouse, but John Hartnup indicated that such a request must be addressed to the Marine Surveyor, Lieutenant M. A. Sweeney R.N., or to the Secretary to the Mersey Docks and Harbour Board.

Water leaking into the Domes of the Observatory at times of heavy rain has been an occasional problem throughout the building's history. In October 1885 John Hartnup reported to the Dock Board's civil engineer, W. N. Le Mesurier: -
"The large amount of water which finds its way into the observing rooms appears to be chiefly owing to the doors at the bottom of the dome-shutters not being watertight. It will be a great boon to us if this defect can be remedied as a quantity of water remains on the beds of the domes and interferes with their working in addition to rotting the woodwork. When, two days since, the wood (covers?) were taken off, a large coal-scuttle full of rust was removed and the domes now work much more freely."
Other matters needing attention on that occasion included a worn rope on the transit-shutter, perished india-rubber round the chronometer testing case, worn-out mats at the office entrance and broken glass globes on some of the gas brackets.

Again in March 1886 he reported to Le Mesurier:-
"There is a considerable leak in the pipes, recently put in the hot water apparatus, as soon as the water is allowed to (run?). I mentioned this to Mr. Thompson today and I believe he has given instructions for this matter to be attended to. I however omitted to say that the lead pipe, which supplies hot water to the sinks in the back kitchen, has burst", and in May he reported "Water coming in through the ceiling of the clock room after the rain of the past two days…"

John Hartnup's strict sense of honour is demonstrated in a letter sent to a ship owner in Swansea on August 14th 1885. It reads -
"Dear Sir,
Two shillings have been returned to me by the Railway Company as overcharged on carriage of your two chronometers. This makes the Railway Company's charge for carriage amount to four shillings. One shilling and sixpence was given to the special messenger who brought the instruments to the Observatory which is three miles from the station."
Four days later John Hartnup acknowledged the receipt of five shillings and sixpence in postage stamps sent from the shipowner in Swansea.

He was elected a Fellow of the Royal Astronomical Society on Feb 12, 1886, and he supported the Liverpool Astronomical Society, and for some time was its Vice-president. "Other scientific societies in Liverpool found in him a warm and cordial supporter."

From 1886 John Hartnup relied on an assistant to write out his letters for him, and I was relieved to find that this person's handwriting was much easier to read than that of either of the Hartnups. This assistant was probably 26 year old Fred Skinner. We do not know very much about him, even though he remained on the Observatory staff for more than forty years.

Sir Digby Murray, Bart, requested, via the Marine Surveyor, details of the Observatory's wind readings for the 8th to 10th December 1886, and these were duly provided. However the Marine Surveyor was obviously anxious that information passed to so great a personage as a Baronet (who was an expert on wind pressure as the following extracts reveal) should be beyond question and the ensuing correspondence gives us some insight into the method of measuring the wind in those days:-

John Hartnup's letter to Sir Digby includes the following detail:-

"We have two self-registering instruments, an Osler's anemometer which records the pressure in pounds on the square foot and the direction of the wind, and a Robinson's cup anemometer which records the velocity in miles."

In his attempt to reassure the Marine Surveyor, John Hartnup writes:-

"Referring to your letter of the 18th ultimo in which you kindly sent me an extract from Sir Digby Murray's pocket book on the subject of Wind Pressure, and to our conversation on this matter when I last saw you, Mr. Osler was good enough to personally superintend the construction and erection of our anemometer - the springs which carry the Pressure Plate have been repeatedly tested and the instruments have been examined by several scientists since.

When he was Secretary to the Committee appointed to consider the question of Wind Pressure on Railway structures, Mr. Wilfred Airy visited this Observatory and carefully examined our arrangements for (recording?) the pressure, direction and velocity of the wind. It was W. Airy's opinion that the exposed position of the anemometers was sufficient to account for the high pressures and velocities which they have recorded on several occasions.

In the report which we send you daily at 9 a.m. the extreme pressure of the wind is given for any instant during the preceding 24 hours. The greatest and least velocity of the wind is also given: this, however, is not for any instant but for the whole hour between any hour and the next hour following. I think this ought to be explained because persons misunderstand the information supplied and think the results (in error?) when such is not the case."

In those days the meteorological charts were carefully bound for preservation, as indicated in a memo to The Liverpool Printing and Stationery Company in February 1887:-

"Herewith I send you the Anemometer and Barometer sheets for the year 1886 - for binding according to patterns sent. Kindly get them finished at your earliest, since the records may at any moment be required for reference." A few of these bound volumes still survive into the 21st Century, but they are badly de-composed. The binding of charts seems to have ceased quite early on, but the daily weather reports have been bound into annual volumes right up to the closure of the weather station. Unfortunately many of the earlier volumes were lost, but the statistics, which were abstracted and recorded separately, have thankfully survived.

John Hartnup had at least two assistants - Fred Skinner and W. P. Hale.

On one occasion in 1889 the Astronomer's deputy (probably Fred Skinner) was called upon to give evidence at St. Helen's Crown Court. He took with him the anemometer sheets for 1888 - a "heavy volume" - thus incurring the expense of railway fare, cab hire and "porterage", a total cost of ten shillings and sixpence. During Skinner's absence the Astronomer was occupied with the routine duties of the Observatory. For this inconvenience it was decided reluctantly to charge the client the sum of one guinea.

The delicate nature of chronometer mechanisms is revealed in a letter sent to Messrs Reid & Sons of Newcastle upon Tyne in September 1889:-
"In future it would be best for you to arrange with your Liverpool Agent to receive any Chronometers you may wish to have tested here and superintend their transit between the Observatory and the Railway Station. A Parcel Delivery Company cart is not a safe mode of conveyance for marine Chronometers at all events when 'going'. The instruments in question however do not appear to have suffered in transit."

An interesting letter to Mr. Russell, headmaster of St. Mary's School, Edge Hill, sent in 1889, about a planned visit by a

group of pupils on 21st December, says:-
"If the sky is clear I will also arrange for them to be shown a star through the Equatorial Telescope. Between 11a.m. and noon or 1 and 3 p.m. would be the most convenient time." This confirms previous indications that the telescope could be used to observe stars in daylight.

A group from the YMCA, Mount Pleasant, Liverpool, wished to tour the Observatory on Easter Monday 1890, but were informed that John Hartnup had given his assistants leave of absence on that day. A second party asked to come on Good Friday or Easter Monday and were given the same response. This reveals that, in those days, leave of absence, even on Good Friday, was at the discretion of the Astronomer.
All requests to visit the Observatory (and there were many of them) were received by telegram, via the Mersey Docks and Harbour Board, during the Hartnup eras.

Defending the system of rating chronometers to Henry Dent Gardner Esq. in 1890, John Hartnup indicated that Bidston's method of rating in "the definite and equidistant temperature" had recently been adopted at the United States Naval Observatory at Washington in order to determine the temperature coefficients of the Chronometers employed in the U.S.Navy, and pointed out that Marine Chronometers were tested at Kew in a similar fashion.

Writing to A. B. Forwood, Esq. (a Liverpool M. P.) he defended the Bidston procedure even more strongly:-

"Dear Sir,

In reply to your letter - It is well known to all conversant with such matters that chronometer makers take very great pains both as to the workmanship and the adjustments of the chronometers which they send to the Royal Observatory for competition at the annual trials ---. Temperature corrections can generally be applied with advantage to the rates of even the best and most carefully compensated chronometers.

To efficiently determine these corrections it is absolutely necessary that the chronometers be rated in a systematic manner in definite and equidistant temperatures in order to eliminate the change of rate due to change of temperature from irregularities of performance arising from other causes.

My father, who was Director of this Observatory from its establishment in 1843 until 1885, devised such a system about 20 years since. This form of Test has been adopted at the Washington Observatory for chronometers employed in the U.S. Navy.

Chronometers sent to this Observatory naturally vary greatly as regards the regularity of their daily rates - some go very indifferently while in many cases the performance is excellent - The Test Certificate shows whether a chronometer is a good timekeeper or otherwise and also gives the necessary data for calculating the temperature corrections which generally remain almost constant for years.

It is very desirable that these corrections should be determined after the instrument has been repaired or cleaned though it by no means follows that they must necessarily have changed materially even under such conditions.

I do not regard the system of applying temperature corrections to the rates of chronometers merely as a means of obtaining fairly good results from inferior instruments but as a most valuable help to the more accurate carrying on of the Greenwich Time at sea, when the best and most carefully adjusted chronometers are employed.

Herewith I send you two reports, one by the late Director of this Observatory and the other by myself. The latter consists principally of meteorological results but I have devoted a few pages to the subject of chronometers.

I should much like to show you the arrangements at this Observatory for testing chronometers - I am quite sure that we could render still further service to mercantile navigation if Shipowners and Shipmasters would interest themselves more in this matter."

In June he reported to the Dock Board's Civil Engineer that: "the outside painting of the Observatory requires attention, and also that the material which covers the floors in the offices of instrument-testing, and which was put down soon after the erection of the Observatory at Bidston has almost entirely perished. I should be greatly obliged if something can be done on this matter as it is impossible to keep the place clean under such conditions." Following this a Komptalicon cutting sample was sent to Messrs J. & R. Smith of Williamson Square, and linoleum was to be provided for the stairs.

In 1891 the Equatorial telescope needed attention for the first time since it had been installed at Bidston in 1866. Sir Howard Grubb supervised the repairs, and the telescope was out of action for six months. This was a frustrating time for hopeful observers such as the Liverpool Science Students' Association.

John Hartnup wrote to the Marine Surveyor on February 22nd 1892 on the subject of the time gun:-
"The time gun as observed from Bidston on Friday and Saturday last was slightly in advance of the normal clock but not so much as a second. There is nothing wrong with the battery here and the gun clock is in coincidence with the normal clock. I will have the exploder contacts at the gun clock examined this morning."

On March 12th 1892 he wrote to the YMCA at Mount Pleasant, Liverpool, re-iterating that only small parties of visitors to the Observatory were acceptable, and on April 11th he arranged for a party to visit on the following Saturday.

Sadly, however, John Hartnup died tragically at Bidston a few days later on 21st April 1892 at the early age of 51. I cannot do better than reproduce the reports of the event from the local newspaper:-

"DREADFUL FATALITY ON BIDSTON HILL
(Birkenhead News - 23rd April 1892)[1]
Fall of an Astronomer from the Observatory Roof

A great deal of excitement prevailed in and about the peaceful little village of Bidston on Thursday, upon it becoming known that one of the most highly respected residents of the district, Mr. John Hartnup, director of the Mersey Docks and Harbour Board's Observatory at Bidston Hill, had met with a fearful and untimely death at an early hour in the morning.

The deceased gentleman, who was about 50 years of age, was married but had no family. He was of an amiable and retiring disposition, and endeared himself with all with whom he came in contact.

It seems that it was part of Mr. Hartnup's duty to inspect from time to time, day and night, the anemometers which are placed on the flat roof of the building, and which register automatically the force and direction of the wind. The driving portions of these instruments are a set of fan wheels and a set of cups, so arranged as to catch the wind; and in the lower rooms the motions are registered by pencils upon drums of prepared paper. In order to ensure accuracy in the calculations it is absolutely necessary that these fan wheels and cups are continually moving; and accordingly Mr. Hartnup went up to the roof between six and seven o'clock on Thursday morning to examine them as he was accustomed to do.

Meantime, expecting every minute that he would come down to his breakfast, his wife and sister-in-law were waiting in the lower portion of the premises, which forms the residence. As he did not come the sister-in-law opened the door to look out, and was horrified to see Mr. Hartnup just falling from the roof on to the ground. An alarm was raised immediately, and the others about the place came and removed the body into the house, while a servant was despatched in a cab for Dr. Harris, of Devonshire Place, who, upon arrival pronounced life to be extinct. The skull was fractured, the neck dislocated, and the wrists were broken. The doctor expressed the opinion that Mr. Hartnup had been looking up towards the instruments, and that in stepping backwards to obtain a better view he walked against the coping stone, which is comparatively low, and being seized with a fit of dizziness, he over-balanced himself, and fell over to the ground, a depth of thirty-one feet. The district coroner, Mr. Henry Churton, held an inquest the same evening at the Observatory, when Kathleen Hammond, sister-in-law of the deceased, gave evidence as to seeing Mr. Hartnup on the roof as was his custom, looking at the anemometers, when he tumbled sideways over the ledge, 20 inches high, which ran round the roof. The deceased had always considered the place dangerous, and had warned witness against going too near the wall. Lately he had been subjected to severe attacks of dizziness. On the previous day he and witness were going for a drive to New Brighton, but when they reached Wallasey he became dazed and she had to take the reins and drive home. On Sunday last when they were out for a walk he was similarly attacked.

Mr. Churton said the 20-inch wall was quite insufficient protection for a place of that description. Still the deceased, he was told, never complained to the Dock Board of the danger, and he almost wondered that a man who had arrived at the deceased's time of life had not considered it a part of his duty to make a representation of the danger to the proper quarter. He had very little doubt that the giddiness spoken of had contributed to the accident. Most likely the immediate cause of death was the breaking the neck. There was no positive evidence to prove the fact, but the deceased had fallen from the roof, and death had followed, and if the jury were satisfied that he was accidentally killed, the verdict would be clear enough.

A verdict of accidental death was recorded, and a rider was added, calling the attention of the Mersey Dock Board to the danger of the position, and asking the authority to remedy it as quickly as possible.

Mr. W.C.Thorne, assistant solicitor to the Board, stated that he would make the presentments, and he did not doubt that anything that ought to be done would be done, and in the shortest possible time."

The report does not tell us which of the three doors was opened by the sister-in-law, so it is not possible to know on which side of the building the Director fell. The door to the courtyard is the nearest one to the living accommodation, so it may be that he fell into the courtyard. Bidston's weather records for 23rd April show that the minimum temperature overnight was 42.4°F. There was no rain. So we can rule out the possibility of John Hartnup slipping on an icy or wet surface. The wind was fresh and from a westerly direction between 6 a.m. and 7 a.m., so a gust may have contributed to the fall, but the suggestion of an attack of dizziness seems the most likely explanation for his fall.

From 'People and Saying' - Birkenhead News - Saturday April 23rd 1892 (price one half-penny)[2]
"That the tragic fate of the late Mr. Hartnup has created profound sympathy in all directions. The deceased was a patient worker in the cause of science and had acquired a vast store of useful knowledge. A chat with him on the working and benefits of the Observatory under his charge was a rare treat to a non-scientific man. He was always ready to answer questions, and had the power of making scientific explanations intelligible to ordinary work-a-day folk."

Funeral Report - Birkenhead News - Saturday April 30th 1892
"The funeral took place on Monday afternoon, April 25th, at the Bidston churchyard. The coffin was carried from the deceased's residence to the churchyard by six bearers, and among those who met it at the gate were many members of the Dock Board, personal friends, and officials of the Observatory and elsewhere, among whom Mr. Hartnup had during his lifetime gained the highest esteem. The Rev. F.J. Buckler, rector of Bidston, conducted the funeral ceremony."

The following were among the mourners who followed the body from the Observatory to the church -

Mr. William Hammond & Miss Hammond (brother-in-law and sister-in-law) & F. Skinner (Assistant Astronomer). There is no mention of John Hartnup's widow being there - perhaps she was too upset to attend.

I have no knowledge of how heavy a gentleman John Hartnup was, but, even if he was lightweight, it must have been quite an ordeal to carry the coffin down the hill from the Observatory to the village, a distance of about half a mile, over rough ground, particularly as the weather report tells us that there was a strong W'ly or WNW'ly wind blowing that afternoon.

Many people met the cortege at the church - Members of the Dock Board, Secretary of the Dock Board, the Dock Board Engineer, the Chief Accountant, the Treasurer, the Marine Surveyor, F. H. Osler (the inventor of the anemometer of that name?), William Brown, G. Royden and the Mayor of Birkenhead.

The coffin was of polished oak with brass mountings, and bore the simple inscription "John Hartnup, died 21st April 1892, aged 51 years."

Numerous wreaths were sent by scientific & personal friends of the deceased. Funeral arrangements were carried out by Messrs. G. H. Lee & Co, Basnett St. Liverpool - a company which would continue to trade under that name until the year 2002!

John Hartnup's gravestone can still be seen in the grounds of Bidston church. The name of John Hartnup Senior is also inscribed on the stone.

Chapter Seven

Life at Bidston in the Late 19th Century

Following the death of John Hartnup Junior in April 1892, the work of the Observatory had to carry on as usual. This is demonstrated in a letter from his senior assistant, Fred Skinner, to the Secretary of the Dock Board, dated May 3rd:-

"I beg to inform you in reply to your memo of 7th March last that Messrs. Leyton and Steel have today served a subpoena for the attendance of myself or Mr. P. W. Hale at the County Court on Thursday next the 5th inst. at 10.30 a.m. to certify to the records supplied in connection with the rainfall results for the 25th June and the 1st July of last year. I explained the difficulty of my leaving the Observatory and asked if they could arrange with Counsel to accept the certified statement. This they will try to do. If unsuccessful I presume Mr. Hale might attend the Court."

Fred Skinner took charge of the Observatory, signing his letters as "Astronomer - pro temp" or "Director - pro temp."

The widow and sister-in-law of John Hartnup Junior may have vacated the premises quite quickly - a letter written by

Fred Skinner on 20th May says that "there will be no person staying in the house from Saturday afternoon to Monday morning."

In an intriguing letter also dated May 20th, addressed to the Secretary of the Dock Board, Fred Skinner says:-
"I beg to acknowledge receipt of your memo of the 19th instant respecting the various instruments and the Sale. Mr. Leete informed me that owing to the instruments being advertised and his client not having withdrawn their sale, he has no other course than to sell them in an assumed name for the Board. He will communicate with you on the question. The following were the prices obtained:-

498 & 499	Combined Thermometer	25/-
504	Transit Theodolite	£13
505	Artificial Horizon	11/-
507	Gun Metal Sextant Holder	15/-
510	Sidereal Chronometer	£10
517	Spirit Level	9/6d

There is no further enlightenment on this matter. Whether the sale was arranged by John Hartnup Junior before his untimely death (perhaps to raise extra finance), or was a responsibility taken on by Mr. Skinner (to the disapproval of the Dock Board) we cannot know.

On June 3rd Fred Skinner arranged for a party of 30-40 men from the YMCA to visit the Observatory. He evidently did not share the Hartnups' feelings about limiting visitor numbers!

During his time in charge he seems to have experienced some difficulties with the time gun. Between June 28th and July 28th the fuse failed on 11 occasions. For the whole of the following week it was ordered not to be fired. On August 13th he was investigating the problems: - "I will go down to the gun tomorrow if possible by 10 a.m. I cannot leave the Observatory until about 9-15 a.m. because of setting instruments and (taking) readings." Presumably the problem with the gun was then sorted out.

When the Directorship of the Liverpool Observatory was advertised soon afterwards, William Edward Plummer (see Chapter Fourteen) applied for the position and was accepted.

A gentleman called George Higgs also applied for the position of Director. He was given a glowing recommendation by Professor Herschel of Observatory House, Slough, who was probably a grandson of the famous astronomer. Professor Herschel wrote to the Chairman of the Dock Board recommending Mr. Higgs for his "excellent qualifications for filling the appointment, peculiarly belonging to his long experience and practice."[1] Professor Herschel was curtly informed that the letter "would receive the Board's attention." George Higgs must have been very frustrated not to be appointed!

William Edward Plummer

(Courtesy Proudman Oceanographic Laboratory)

Whether Fred Skinner (Director- pro temp), who was ten years younger than Mr. Plummer, actually applied for the position is not known. He may have assumed that, as John Hartnup Junior seems to have taken over from his father without question, so he, as the senior assistant, would automatically take over from John Hartnup Junior. However, this was not to be, but he remained in post as the chief assistant.

William Plummer moved with his family, wife Sarah, daughter Alice (20), and sons Henry Crozier (16) and Paul (8), into the living accommodation at Bidston, and they employed a live-in cook-domestic, Dora Duffin. She was single, aged 39, and a native of Liverpool.

The Bidston Annual Reports for 1892 onwards are signed by W. E. Plummer. They are more concise than previous reports. The report covering 1892, for instance, makes no mention of John Hartnup Junior's accident, although in a short report to the Royal Astronomical Society in 1893 Mr. Plummer says :-

"The digest of meteorological observations made under the superintendence of the late Mr. J. Hartnup in 1889-1891 is now in the press and the results will shortly be sent to those who are sufficiently interested in meteorological work to apply for a copy."

One of the first things Mr. Plummer did was to make an inventory of the instruments, books and property of the Dock Board at Bidston Observatory. Copies of the list, in Plummer's copperplate handwriting, still exist, dated September 1892, with updates in July 1906 and October 1917.

Among the many instruments listed there are upright portable desks, a copying press, postage scales, scales with weights: namely 3 at 56 lbs, 2 at 28 lbs, 1 at 14 lbs, 1 at 7 lbs, 2 at 4 lbs, and 1 at 1 lb, and an oak table with marble top and two oak seats. The list conjures up a picture of a typical Dickensian office.

Mr. Plummer's prescribed duties were to continue the work of his predecessors, namely maintenance of a time service (one o'clock gun, etc), rating of chronometers, and continuation of the meteorological records. The transit telescope, now nearly fifty years old, was checked over and found to be still in good working order, as was the equatorial. Mr. Plummer was able to indulge in his favourite activity of observing comets.

In November 1892 he suggested to the Astronomer Royal that the latitude and longitude of the Observatory should be "accurately determined" using the electric telegraph. This was done the following year.

As far back as 1886 the Chester Solicitors representing Robert C. de Grey Vyner had drawn up plans to sell off Bidston Hill for the development of housing. The increased local population would be served by an additional railway station, to be opened just west of Bidston Village on the new branch line to Upton, and a water tower would be erected on Bidston Hill near the windmill. The plans met strong opposition from conservationists and the "Preservation of Bidston Hill" Society was formed. It was chaired by the Mayor of Birkenhead assisted by the Lord Mayor of Liverpool. £1600 was raised initially with a view to buying the land from Mr. Vyner for the benefit of the public. The plans seem to have been put on hold for seven years due to the opposition, for by 1893 the sum raised had increased to £10,300. This was paid to Mr. Vyner for the purchase of approximately fifty acres extending from Upton Road to the south of the hill to Mr. Vyner's house in the north. The railway station and water tower never materialized.

Also in 1893 Mr. Plummer was elected to Liverpool Physical Society and became President the following year. He was nominated by Sir Oliver Lodge, the first Professor of Physics at Liverpool College. Sir Oliver had been invited to form the Society in order to "cultivate Physical Science in the city" and became its first President in 1889. Sir Oliver was, in 1894, the first man to actually transmit a message by wireless signal.[2]

Mr. Plummer's choice of lecture subjects at the Society reflected his interest in meteorology and natural phenomena. One was entitled "The diurnal variation of the barometer", and another was "The barometer and storms."

For many years Mr. Plummer was Honorary Reader in Astronomy at Liverpool University and he gave lectures with practical demonstrations at the Observatory. The Chester Literary and Philosophical Society awarded him the Kingsley Medal for his contribution to local scientific education, and, having been elected a Fellow of the Royal Astronomical Society in 1879, he served on the Council from 1889 to 1894.

He was President of Liverpool Astronomical Society from 1894-97 and again from 1899-1919. During the intervening two years the Presidency was held by a Mr. G. Higgs. Was this the George Higgs who had unsuccessfully applied for the post of Director at Bidston five years earlier?

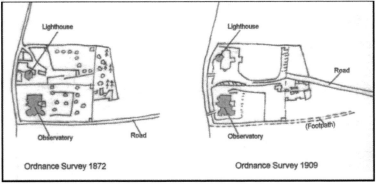

Some time between 1872 and 1909 the road up to the Observatory was re-routed directly up the hill between the new lighthouse and the Observatory. The above diagrams (previously shown in the lighthouse chapter) clearly show the change. The postcard below, dated 1909, shows the old road and the new one.

Two hundred chronometers were tested at the Observatory in 1894. In a memo Plummer points out that "It must be understood that in no sense of the word is a competition instituted as at the Royal Observatory, Greenwich." This re-enforces John Hartnup Junior's earlier comments on the subject of competition.

In a letter sent to the Treasurer of the Dock Board in 1895 Plummer says: "Mr. Skinner will probably present himself tomorrow for the money as usual." This may suggest that Fred Skinner was responsible for collecting the staff wages in person.

Another of Fred Skinner's duties was to sleep at the Observatory whenever Plummer was away for any reason.

This happened occasionally at weekends, and for a fortnight each August while the Plummers went on holiday.

Plummer seems to have been prickly at times (perhaps with justification). This comes across in some of his correspondence:-

In a letter to the Curator of an Art Gallery Mr. Plummer writes:-

"It would have afforded me great pleasure to have given a lecture at the Art Gallery, notwithstanding the smallness of the honorarium, but unfortunately I have not time to prepare it."

In a letter to a Solicitor, dated April 19th 1895, he says:-

"I have been rather surprised that you have never sent me a cheque for expenses as a witness in the case of 'X' versus 'Y'.

It places me in a very undignified position to make a second application. It is like a tradesman dunning for money."

Three months later, having received no response, he wrote again to the solicitors:-

"Gentlemen ....There may of course be some adequate explanation of the long delays but the impression left on my mind is a very unfavourable one.

I strongly suspect that if I had had occasion to employ your time and experience you would have expected adequate compensation before so long an interval. I fail to see wherein the comparison is applicable."

In a memo to a furniture company he says:-

Gentlemen, Messrs 'X', Furniture Removers of Egremont

have this afternoon been here with the bookcase, and demanded from me before delivery the sum of ten shillings.

Holding as I do your receipt for all charges including delivery I am surprised that you should have lent yourselves to such an arrangement and endeavour to make me pay another ten shillings.

I was naturally indignant and refused to pay, the bookcase was taken back to Seacombe and as I understand another ten shillings will be demanded before it can be delivered.

.... the only point that troubles me is that I can conceive that the furniture is suffering from being continuously pulled in and out of vans (horse-drawn?), so further trouble may arise on this account."

The matter of the Observatory window blinds also seems to have troubled him somewhat. Several memos refer to them, and finally in June 1895 he wrote to a Mr. Atkinson, who seems to have been an intermediary:-

"I am very much obliged to you for the trouble you have taken to interest yourself in the matter of the Observatory window blinds. No doubt it will all come right, but in the meantime we suffer grievously.

It was May 6th that I appealed to you and on June 20th we seem to be as far off as ever.

On Monday some six or eight (blinds?) were taken away and are still away. It is an insult to one's intelligence to suppose that some one has been at work on them ever since.

Let one once escape from the hands of this firm and I promise you never to ask for anything again that is likely to bring me in contact with them."

Problems with water supply and sewerage were a constant worry:-

In a letter to the General Manager and Secretary of the Dock Board, Mr. Le Mesurier, Plummer says, "We have had no water supplied by the Town Waterworks to the upper tank for months and it is my intention to lodge a very serious complaint with the authorities. But before I take this step I wish to be assured that no obstruction exists here. The water has been turned on and off more than once to repair pipes and it may be that it is now accidentally shut off. Before I make my complaint I should be glad if you could send up a plumber to make quite certain that the fault does not lie with me."

On April 18th he reported that some officials from the waterworks had been to investigate the water supply. He understood they were going to consult the plumber next day.

In those days relations with the Meteorological Council appear to have been a little bit strained. In a letter to Mr. Le Mesurier written on March 11th 1895 Plummer says:-
"In thinking over our interview this morning, I have to regret that I did not make it clear to you that I am grateful for your attempt to endeavour to improve the strained relations between the Secretary of the Meteorological Council (Mr. Scott) and myself, though you do not find yourself able to give one material support."

An extract from a letter to Mr. Le Mesurier two weeks later reads:-
"It is sufficient for me that in my efforts to work the Board's

Observatory economically and efficiently I find myself hampered by Mr. Scott, who would feign exercise an authority incompatible with what I conceive to be my duties as Director, and as I understand the correspondence the onus is placed upon you to decide whether I am to regard Mr. Scott as chief, or to have a free hand in the conduct of the Observatory.

If, as I confidently expect you are disposed to give me a loyal support, then it seems to me desirable to give Mr. Scott due notice for the determination of the existing arrangement ...."

In a second letter written later that day he says:-

"For your own information I beg to inform you that the real grievance at the bottom of this and other correspondence of a like nature is the fact that Mr. Scott will not recognise the Board's Observatory as one of the first class.

The reputation of the Observatory is increasing and it is galling to be reckoned by the Secretary to the Meteorological Office on the same level as anyone who simply possesses a barometer and a thermometer.

It does not seem to me to be just to the Board .... their annual and generous expenditure to be reckoned on so low a level. Doubtless Mr. Scott is prompted by economical motives, because if the Observatory is placed on the official rank it becomes entitled to an annual fee of £15 for the information supplied."

The matter seems to have been settled amicably, as a letter from Mr. Scott, written one month later, politely acknowledges receipt of meteorological information.

In July 1895 Mr. T. H. Hornby of the Wirral Footpaths Preservation Society sent the following letter to the Director:-

"Dear Sir,

At a meeting of my committee held on 5th Inst. attention was drawn to the overflow and escape of sewage matter on the NE corner of the Dock Board's Enclosure on Bidston Hill, and I was requested to communicate with you giving you notice of the matter complained of and asking your attention thereto."

It is interesting to conjecture what event could have led to the following response by Plummer to a letter from W. Laird Esq.,Shipbuilder, dated April 2nd 1896 :-

"Dear Sir - I am in no way responsible for the accuracy of tidal predictions and I think your question should be addressed to our good friend Lieutenant Strong, the Marine Surveyor.

I am afraid there will always be grievous errors as long as the tides are computed on strictly dynamic lines, that is to say neglecting the profligacy of the wind and barometer.

When I first came down here I was anxious to do something to bring the Observatory into repute and proposed to discuss the effect of such variables, but I was told such discussion would have been only of academic interest for the Board could not accept responsibility in the matter and I consequently let the matter drop.

I still think something might be done to assist unusual cases such as you refer to.

May I add my congratulations on the successful result of floating the Mars (a battleship) notwithstanding?"

Little did he know it then, but the accuracy of tidal predictions would be very much Bidston's responsibility in future years!

In 1896 Plummer advertised a series of lectures to be held at the Observatory on Wednesday evenings at 8-30 pm. The subject for the October term was Spherical Astronomy, including Theory of Instruments and Problems in Nautical Astronomy. In the Lent term the Observatory would be open for practical work and informal instruction would be given. In the summer term lectures would be offered on the History of Astronomy and Meteorology. I do not know how well these lectures were attended, but transport must have been something of a problem, particularly in the winter evenings. Presumably most students walked up from the station.

Plummer was unhappy about the siting of the thermometer 'cage' on the south side of the Observatory, feeling that the instruments were too close to the boundary wall and should have more protection from the sun. In 1897 he experimented by setting a pair of maximum and minimum thermometers on a temporary wooden stand to the north of the Observatory dwelling house, in a position 30 yards to the north of the current cage, and a second pair on a similar stand to the north of the lighthouse building at a distance of 30 yards from the previous point. The experiment continued for one calendar month. Analysis of the results showed that on average the maximum thermometer on the original site was 0.7°F. too high, while the minimum was 1.4°F. too high.

As a result a second cage was made by the carpenter who worked on site. It was erected on the north side of the building (in the first experimental position) in 1897, and for a period of eight years readings were taken from both screens. Finally in 1905 Plummer concluded that the readings from the southern screen were too high due to "radiation from the southern front of the building." From then on only readings from the north screen were used.

On 17th December 1896 a minor earth tremor had affected the accuracy of the transit telescope. This may have influenced the Mersey Docks & Harbour Board to give permission the following year for the installation of a seismograph in the Observatory to measure earthquake waves. The deep cellars, built into the rock, made an ideal location. Plummer was uncertain which cellar to use. He could have used the round cellar under the Equatorial tower or the long "clock cellar" situated at a lower level. He decided on the clock cellar. An instrument was borrowed from the British Association for the Advancement of Science, and was set up in September that year. Plummer assured the Mersey Docks and Harbour Board that "The Instrument would be here on loan, and no expense would be incurred in connection with the observations. The registration is automatic, but in any case the observation would not be allowed to interfere with either my duties or those of my assistant." Earthquakes near Tashkent (September 17th) and Port-au-Prince (December 29th) were recorded in 1898.

A letter from Plummer to the Observatory Committee of the Dock Board in April 1897 requests: "Will you please send to have the midden emptied at your earliest convenience. Also to send a supply of firewood. I think the wood had better not be cut up - there may be a tendency to use it extravagantly when it is so easily handled." In another letter on May 3rd that same year he wrote: "I think the cesspools should be examined as I hear complaints." A survey of the area, dated 1898, shows that there were six cesspools on the site. These were later filled in.[3]

In 1897 gates were erected across the roadway leading up to the Observatory (possibly those shown on the postcard - right). To quote Plummer - "Unfortunately

Card postmarked 1909

the gates have been made to open up the hill. The consequences of this are that when open they rest on higher ground than when shut. In order therefore to set them open, it has been necessary to cut away the roadway and this has been left in

Above - The same view nearly 100 years later

a very unsatisfactory condition, leaving practically a little step, thus breaking the continuity of the roadway and making the passageway of vehicles still more inconvenient than before."

In a letter sent to the Observatory many years later in <u>1982</u> a retired sea captain, living locally, recalled how in 1920 he was sent to Bidston as a young Merchant Navy cadet, accompanying an officer, to deliver three ship's chronometers for rating. They travelled up to the Observatory by horse-drawn cab, carrying the chronometers on cushions to prevent jolting. Hopefully, the problem of the uneven roadway had been resolved many years earlier!

The responsibility for opening and shutting the gates leading up to the Observatory seems to have been quite a source of irritation to Mr. Plummer. In a letter to the Dock Board in March 1898 he says:

"I received a verbal message, through the Policeman in charge of the Bidston Hill Recreation Ground, that the Dock Board has given instructions that the gate across the road leading to the Observatory was to be kept shut. This, as you know, is to misrepresent the concession granted by the Board, which goes no further than saying that there is no objection to the gate being closed. I imagine such a form of words implies that the authorities in charge of the ground may direct their own officers to close the gate. It certainly does not authorise these officers to order members of my family to do so, and I should imagine that such conduct would not be approved by you. If I am right in my conjecture you will take the necessary steps to prevent a repetition of such conduct on the part of the Officers under your control."

The Director presumably did the weekend meteorological observations himself. A letter written by Plummer to the

Mersey Docks and Harbour Board in May 1898 requested permission to "sleep away from the Observatory on the nights of Saturday and Sunday the 14th and 15th instant. I propose to leave here after 2 pm on Saturday returning early on Monday, the usual arrangements having been made for the necessary observations in my absence." (In other words Fred Skinner would step into the breach).

Plummer continued the practice of inviting parties up to the Observatory for Saturday afternoon visits. Details of one such visit - numbers limited to 50 at a charge of 2/6d each - was given in The British Association Excursion Guide Book - First Edition - 1896:[4]

"Time Table

2-30 p.m. Steamer to Birkenhead from Landing Stage.

2-45 p.m. Waggonettes leave for Bidston Hill.

3-15 p.m. Arrive Bidston Hill Observatory, where Messrs. Bushell and Plummer will receive the visitors. Afternoon tea will be kindly provided.

5-15 p.m. Waggonettes leave for Birkenhead.

6-10 p.m. Arrive at Liverpool Landing Stage.

During the afternoon Plummer gave a detailed talk on the history and present workings of the Observatory. Following this the more energetic visitors were taken on a guided tour of the hill and Flaybrick to view the geology of the area".

On other occasions visitors arrived by steam train using the new Wirral Railway. One party comprised 13 members of the Liverpool Physical Society, who travelled to Wirral by train on 9th December 1899.

Correspondence passed between Plummer and Dr. Copeland, Astronomer Royal for Scotland, in 1899, on the possible siting of an earthquake observatory. The type of rock foundation proved to be the big issue. Dr. Copeland felt that Bidston's sandstone rock would be much more continuous than the Scottish basalt, which was full of fissures. It was suggested that a Milne siesmograph be tested at each site for six months. However, despite Bidston's sandstone base, a site near Edinburgh was finally selected for the earthquake observatory.

(In the 21st Century the Institute of Geological Sciences, the British Centre for the monitoring of earthquakes, is still located near Edinburgh. Both sites, Edinburgh and Bidston, were component Institutes of the Natural Environment Research Council).

In August 1895 Plummer had been appointed Examiner in Astronomy at the University of Edinburgh and in March 1900 he was offered an honorary appointment as Reader in Astronomy by the Vice Chancellor of University College, London. As a salaried officer of the Dock Board he had to ask the Board's permission before accepting these appointments.

It seems that a few weeks later there were plans to install an electricity generator at Bidston to replace gas. At first Mr. Plummer had reservations on the subject. He may have feared that the vibrations would upset the scientific instruments. However, in reply to a memo from the Dock Board he said he was "compelled to admit that the instruments in the Observatory would not be affected by the proposed electrical installation", but perhaps in future Bidston may "maintain magnetical observations" - "it is most desirable that efficient protection should now be secured." His added comment is intriguing: "It is desirable to strengthen the hands of the Observatory in their fight with the electric companies." Whether an electricity generator was installed at that time is not obvious, but I note that gas mantles were still listed on the inventory seven years later in 1906.

In a letter to a chronometer maker Plummer says - "The chronometers are generally brought here by hand, but your best way would be to put them under charge of the guard of a train, and, on timely notice being given to me, I would meet the train at Woodside, Birkenhead, and bring them up here, provided two or more chronometers were sent at the same time." (The charge for testing chronometers at that time was ten shillings).

Shortly after this he showed rather less enthusiasm for railway employees. In a complaint to the manager of the Wirral Railway he says:-

"I am sorry to have to lodge a complaint against one of the officials at the Docks Station for incompetency and incivility. The circumstances are these -

I travelled on Friday night to the Central Station and was charged for first class return ticket one shilling. I travelled on Saturday, same route, same ticket, and was charged 1/1d [about 40 pence extra in modern terms]. I remonstrated, pointing out that I was either served by an incompetent person who did not know the fare, and actually marked the ticket one shilling, or I was being overcharged on the present occasion. I do not see my escape from this dilemma. But the official was simply noisy and abusive and loudly demanded the payment of the penny of which he intimated that I defrauded the Company on the Friday night. I paid the penny, that was not the point at all, I am not afraid you will think that."

Chapter Eight

The Early 20th Century

The 1901 census reveals that William Plummer's three children were all living at the Observatory at that time. His daughter Alice, now 29, had no occupation outside the home. His elder son Henry Crozier Keating, 25, was a demonstrator in physics, possibly at Liverpool College (the future University), and Paul, aged 17, was an articled accountant. Henry Crozier was destined to be Astronomer Royal for Ireland from 1912 - 1921.

Three families occupied the lighthouse cottages in 1901. They were:-

1. David Chambers, who was still the head telegraph keeper. He lived in cottage no.1 with his wife Catherine and daughter Ellen aged 24. Ellen was a teacher of music "on her own account."

2. Ernest Austin, deputy keeper, a single man of 24, living alone in cottage no. 2.

3. J.H.Askew, lighthouse telegraphist, who lived in cottage no. 3 with his wife and daughter Florence aged 18 (a pupil teacher), and his son, Paul, aged 10.

Braehead Cottage, Bidston Hill

Braehead Cottage (see picture which is postmarked 1909), sited alongside the main drive up to the Observatory, was occupied by William Harris, classed as a labourer/navvy, aged 64, and his wife Ellen aged 63. They apparently had two servants, Alice Gordoodier aged 21 and Susy Satcliffe aged 16. William Graves, aged 27, and Thomas Hardman aged 25, boarded at Braehead. They were classed as head gardener and domestic servant, and gardener and domestic servant respectively. It seems reasonable to assume they were employed by John McGregor Laird, noted shipbuilder and engineer, who lived at Bidston Court with his wife, Theodocia, three children, a niece and a staff of nine servants.

Braehead Cottage served teas, as indicated by the sign on the front of the building. This continued for many years. I recall my parents walking up the hill to join me at lunchtime in the early 1960s, and having a cup of tea at Braehead.

Unfortunately, the cottage has been so badly damaged by vandals in more recent years that it has had to be pulled down.

In 1900 Bidston obtained its own Milne-Seismograph, and tables of observations were published from 1901. Two years later Plummer reported that the "number of earthquakes recorded at Bidston is somewhat greater than at the other British Stations."   Large earthquakes were noted at San Francisco and at Valparaiso in 1905, whilst in that same year Mr. Plummer reported: "It is interesting and important to notice that many earthquakes recorded by the exploring party in the Antarctic Expedition under Commander Scott R.N. were registered on the instrument at Bidston although intermediate stations did not in all instances record the tremors."

Mr. Plummer worried about the financial situation of the Observatory, and made savings wherever possible. In the five years 1885-1890, while John Hartnup Junior was Director, the total cost of instruments, coal, books, stationery, stamps, cleaning and one o'clock gun maintenance, had averaged £315 per annum. By 1895-1900 this had been cut back to an average £184 per annum.

Nonetheless in 1902 the Mersey Docks and Harbour Board made plans to sell the Observatory at Bidston, and drew up proposals for a bill to that effect to be promoted in the next session of Parliament. It is interesting to note that an Act of Parliament was needed to authorise the closure in 1902. (This apparently did not apply in 2004, when the Observatory was closed without Act of Parliament!).

The purpose of the bill was as follows: "To relieve the Board from all obligation to maintain the Observatory on Bidston Hill and to authorise the Board to sell and dispose of the same and the site thereof, and the instruments and the appurtenances therein." The press understood that the Board did not contemplate the erection of a new Observatory.[1]

The Board had been responsible for the Liverpool Observatory since taking over the Waterloo Dock site from Liverpool Corporation in 1858, and when the new building was constructed on Bidston Hill in 1866 it was anticipated that it would become self-supporting. However this had not happened. In the nine years preceding 1901 total running costs had exceeded £9000, while income from the servicing of chronometers and other instruments and the sale of meteorological information during that time accounted for not more than £638 (see chapter Twenty). Costs were increasing, but income was falling. The advent of reliable clocks in the city meant that fewer chronometers were being sent to Bidston for testing. The Dock Board felt that "meteorological observations could be taken with equal accuracy elsewhere", and the Dock Board's "interest in the unfelt tremors of the earth was not immediate."

Plummer wrote to the press, objecting to the fact that Astronomy had been overlooked, and that there was no reference to all the lecture work done in connection with Liverpool College. The plans caused an outcry. The Liverpool Mercury reported on November 21st that "the announcement has been received in Liverpool and Birkenhead with feelings of dismay, not unmingled with disgust." The dismay was due to "apprehensions that the picturesque structure would be devoted to other and baser uses." There were protests from, among others, the Liverpool Astronomical Society and Sir Thomas Maclear, formerly Her Majesty's Astronomer at the Cape of Good Hope, who maintained that "the exertions made at the Liverpool Observatory in testing chronometers were of national importance, and that they deserved some public acknowledgment from the British Government." The National Physical Laboratory at Teddington pointed out that seismological observations at Bidston were of a real value to science and that it would be a loss if they ceased."

A spokesman from the Observatory said:-
"It is highly improbable that the Observatory will be taken over by the Government. The most reasonable and practical suggestion is that the new Liverpool University should seek this medium of scientific instruction. The Observatory was originally founded by the Corporation of Liverpool as owners of the Liverpool Docks and administrators of the affairs of the port, and in going to Parliament for power to get rid of the Observatory the Dock Board is seeking, more than forty years after the event, to vary the terms on which the Dock Estate was acquired and to abolish a public institution that Liverpool created."[2]

The Parliamentary Committee of the Liverpool Corporation made it known to the Mersey Docks and Harbour Board that it had strong objections to the proposals, and would oppose the Bill if it was presented to Parliament, but suggested collaboration with University College (the future University of Liverpool).

The Marine Committee of the Dock Board was itself split over the issue, and the Board was anxious not to upset the Corporation at this time because it particularly wanted Bootle, with its dock system, to be accepted within the Liverpool town boundary. As a result the plans to offload Bidston Observatory were dropped!

However the suggested link with the new University did go ahead. In November 1903 it was decided that:-

1. The Dock Board would grant a lease of the Observatory to the University at a peppercorn rent for 21 years.
2. The University Authority would pay all rates and taxes and do all necessary repairs.
3. The University would employ William E. Plummer and Fred Skinner at their present salaries.
4. The Dock Board would pay £800 per annum towards the upkeep of the Observatory.

In March 1903 Plummer wrote to Professor G. H. Darwin of Cambridge expressing concern that two sets of tidal predictions for Liverpool were in circulation, one from Holdens and one in the Admiralty Tables. The predictions differed in datum and meridians. Plummer asked if Professor Darwin, "speaking from an intimate knowledge of the state of tide calculations", could say that "the necessary data for accuracy exists, or whether any means could be adopted to ensure uniformity in the predictions." The Professor's response is not recorded.

The 1902 tribute from the National Physical Laboratory at Teddington proved to be justified, for on April 8th 1906 the major earthquake in San Francisco, measuring 8.3 on the Richter scale, was recorded at Bidston. The effect began at 0123 GMT and lasted 4 hours 6 minutes. The maximum effect was at 0158 GMT, but the amplitude could not be measured because the trace exceeded the width of the paper on the Observatory's seismograph. The same problem was experienced on August 17th that year, when a major earthquake occurred at Valparaiso, measuring 8.6 on the Richter scale. This started at 0035 GMT, and lasted 3 hours 55 minutes. The maximum effect was at 0150 GMT, and again the amplitude was lost due to limitations on paper width.

Large tremors at Messina, Sicily, on December 28th 1908 and at Abruzzi, Italy, on January 13th 1915 were also recorded at Bidston.

Fires have always occurred on Bidston Hill, as the picture shows. It is taken from a postcard bearing the postmark 1906, and is a reminder of an event reported in the Daily

Courier back in April 1875. On that occasion Mr. H. T. C. Vyner sued two men for "negligently setting fire to his plantation on Bidston Hill." Following a full day's trial at Birkenhead County Court, one offender was fined £50 and the other was discharged. However, Mr. Vyner "in the most generous manner" released the culprit from payment of the fine because honour had been satisfied when the man wrote him a letter of apology.

A press statement read; "We hope that when the public are engaging themselves upon Bidston Hill they will recollect that they are indebted to Mr. Vyner for the privilege, and that he might deprive them of it at any moment, and therefore that it behoves them to testify their appreciation of Mr. Vyner's liberality by strictly following the directions of the notice boards and by refraining from acts which will damage the property, and, as far as they can, assist in preventing others from doing wrong."[3]

Filed away in the Vyner papers is another letter which reveals that the above statement was written by Mr. Vyner's agent rather than by a Daily Courier correspondent. It says that Mr. Vyner was only prepared to waive the £50 fine if the statement were published.[4]

Fires were presumably quite unusual occurrences then, as suggested by the large gathering of onlookers. Regrettably, hill fires are much more common these days. They are often started by arsonists, and hardly attract a passing glance.

In 1909 Professor Milne wrote to Mr. Plummer saying: "If the British Association will provide a quick receiving recorder (a seismograph), would you be inclined to try it on your foundation? As you know I fancy you can pick up with it even smaller records than you get at present."

Plummer replied that he would be "very happy to try a more sensitive instrument" and had plenty of room for it in the basement. A second seismograph was duly installed

under Professor Milne's supervision. It had a horizontal pendulum at an angle of 90° to the original instrument. This second instrument gave the first indication that the weight of tidal water was causing the Wirral Peninsula to oscillate twice a day.

However this seismograph was dismantled in 1913, because the angular measurement had proved a problem.

A Campbell-Stokes sunshine recorder

Bidston's first sunshine recorder (a Campbell-Stokes Recorder) was provided by Mr. Eric Robson and installed on the roof of the anemometer cabin in 1907. Readings began on January 1st 1908. It was soon realised that the domes, rising 20 feet above roof level, obscured the recorder from the sun's rays in the mornings and late afternoons during the winter months, so the recorder was re-sited on the roof itself each winter from September to March, close to the southern parapet.

Many years later, as the trees matured around the Observatory, the parapet site became unsuitable, and a new winter location was found on the narrow ledge encircling the eastern dome.

The card was changed daily at sunset, and to access the recorder the observer had to open a small door in the dome and lean out of a window. This practice was to continue right up to the late 1990s, by which time an automatic system of sunshine measurement had been installed. Perhaps this was well timed because, as the photograph below reveals, the trees are so tall in 2006 that now the eastern dome windows are shaded from the early morning sunshine in winter.

From July 1908 the "character of the sea disturbance" at Formby 'Lightship' was telephoned to Bidston each day, and then transmitted to the Meteorological Office.

Longitude was still being calculated using the Transit telescope and the Bond clock.

When Bidston lighthouse ceased operating in 1913 and was to be "abandoned as a telegraph station on or after October 9th", Plummer was worried on financial grounds. The daily telegram was routinely submitted to the Meteorological Service at South Kensington at 7am each day, free of charge, via the lighthouse telegraph system. This had been the custom since 1903. To quote Mr. Plummer, "I presume that after October 9th the message will be sent by telephone to Birkenhead Post Office .... At present these telegrams are carried free, and in any future arrangements that privilege would no doubt be secured?" The answer to this question is not recorded.

In 1910 it was proposed to set up a wireless installation at Bidston to receive time signals from the Eiffel Tower in Paris and from Nordleich in Germany each morning. This actually happened in 1913, and the information was being used in yet another re-calculation of the longitude of the Observatory. However, on the declaration of war in 1914, the apparatus had to be dismantled by order of the Postmaster General. An interesting letter from Mr. Plummer, addressed to the Secretary of the Post Office, London, requested that the apparatus be taken away, as, although the aerial had been removed, "any mischievous person could easily connect the positions left with a temporary wire, and utilise it for the receipt of messages." He added that "while the Observatory was in the occupation of the Military this seemed of little consequence, but now that they have withdrawn the responsibility is more that I care to shoulder." This is the only suggestion we have that the Military ever occupied the Observatory. In view of the fact that they withdrew at the outbreak of war, their purpose in being there is not obvious.

By modern standards the running costs of the Observatory at that time seem quite modest. An average monthly expenditure in 1906 had amounted to £3-17-0. This might comprise 6/- per week wage for the charwoman, 2/6 per week for the fires and 15/- per month for postage stamps.

Carriage of parcels such as "Greenwich volumes", purchase of gas mantles, and fares for regular trips to Liverpool and Rock Ferry accounted for the rest of the money. It is not clear what institute was situated in Rock Ferry. An extra expense in January 1909 was the cleaning of the Observatory flues - 17/6. For several years the fires had been fuelled by anthracite on the advice of the Dock Board, because it was considered to be more economical than coal.

Life at Bidston does not seem to have been greatly affected by the First World War. (The situation was to be very different in the Second World War). Mr. Plummer, now 65 years of age, continued with normal routine, apart from minor irritations such as having to abandon the longitude exercise, and no longer having the ability to pick up the deduced weather forecast issued by radio telegraph daily at 10 am from the Admiralty station at Cleethorpes. These restrictions were both due to the dismantling of the wireless station. The number of chronometers and sextants being sent to the Observatory for testing showed a slight decrease owing to war restrictions. The firing of the one o'clock gun was unaffected.

On the astronomical front Mr. Plummer was concerned in 1916 that the "police regulations for obscuring artificial light had greatly interfered with the extra-meridial observations", and the Berliner Jahrbuch, a German almanac, was no longer available for consultation. This publication had been available up to the year 1916, so presumably the almanacs were printed several years in advance.
Mr. Plummer reported that, towards the end of 1917, the Meteorological Service (now part of the Air Ministry) required weather reports at 1 a.m., 7a.m., 1 p.m., 6 p.m. and 9 p.m. "for

military purposes" (previously these had only been supplied by Bidston at 7 a.m.). Meteorological information was also being provided to "military centres in the neighbourhood, for assistance in their several duties."

Economies were necessary during the war. In reply to a memo from the General Manager and Secretary of the Dock Board, dated 22nd July 1918, Mr. Plummer says:
"The authorized supplies of coal and gas for the Observatory and house are as follows:-

Coal for the Observatory -	7 tons
Coal for domestic purposes -	9 tons
Gas for the Observatory -	15,000 cubic feet
Gas for the house -	15,000 cubic feet

I find that the annual supply of coal hitherto has been 20 tons for both the Observatory and the house and the gas consumption has been 150,000 cubic feet.

Even with the additional allowance of 5 tons of coal, the deficiency is marked, but last year with 20 tons of coal and a supply of slack and coke the quantity was eked out. The gas consumption is mainly for the chronometer ovens and I see no way by which the necessary amount can be brought within the requirements of the Regulations. Small economies might be effected by putting a smaller gas stove in one of the upper rooms, and a gas stove in the kitchen, thus diminishing the coal to an extravagant kitchen and reducing the time in which the latter is in use. Perhaps in one of the living rooms a gas stove might replace a large uneconomical grate. The supply of gas would be very slightly increased, but the coal supply would be reduced in greater proportion.

W. E. Plummer"

On the 12th November 1918, a day after war ended, Mr. Plummer wrote to the Mersey Docks and Harbour Board saying: "When practically a year ago the Meteorological Office asked the Observatory to furnish weather telegrams at 1 am the arrangement was distinctly understood to be for the service of the military authorities in France during the war.

These telegrams have been furnished without interruption since December 1917, but have taxed the slender staff very severely.

I now propose with your approval to write to the Director of the Meteorological Office requesting to be released from the onerous undertaking at the earliest opportunity consistent with national requirements."

Chapter Nine

Bidston: The Inter-War Period

William Hutchinson, the Liverpool Dockmaster who had experimented with the first reflecting mirror lights in 1763, was very keen on making observations of the tide. Between 1768 and 1793 he observed the high tide levels at the Old Dock Gates close to his home in Liverpool. His tidal observations were used by George and Richard Holden, as a basis for their first Liverpool tide tables, produced about 1769.[1]

On September 6th 1769 the Common Council ordered that "Mr. George Holden be paid the sum of Ten Guineas out of the Dock Dues for making a Tide Table for Liverpool and the like sum of Ten Guineas a year for making a New Tide Table for Liverpool every the first day of August ensuing till further notice."[2]

Hutchinson wrote the preface to the first edition of the tide tables. In it he said: "Thus deficient are all former methods in computing only the times of high water; as for the height, the calculation thereof has never before been attempted by anyone that I know of, though they are, as I apprehend, equally necessary. For of what advantage can it be to the seaman, to know when the tide will be at the highest, if there will not be, at that time, depth of water sufficient for his purpose? Indeed it would be of no more service to know that there would be depth enough of water, unless he knew at the same time, when to expect it. But to know what height the tide will rise to, and at what time, must contribute greatly to his security, and is it not absolutely requisite that a tide table should inform him of both these?"

For a long time the tables were very basic. A paragraph accompanying the 1847 table reads - "In this tide table are only given the heights (in feet and inches) of those tides which come between the hours of six in the morning and six in the evening, which will always be sufficient, as the night tides may be known accurately enough from them being somewhat lower in the months of January, February, March, April, November and December and higher in the other months."

For many years the production of tidal prediction must have been a very laborious business for the Holdens, all calculations being done using pen and paper.

A paper by Lieutenant W. Lord, R.N. presented in 1853 (presumably the same William Lord who had published a code of semaphore signals in 1840), describes the self-registering tide gauges which had recently been installed in the area, one at St. George's Dock, Liverpool and the other on Hilbre Island. The data from these gauges was used, in conjunction with wind and barometric pressure readings from the Waterloo Dock Observatory, to check Holden's tidal predictions.

The Holden family continued the business of producing tidal almanacs for over 180 years.

Professor Joseph Proudman
(Courtesy Proudman Oceanographic Laboratory)

Prior to the 20th century research into tides had been largely confined to individual scientists such as Lord Kelvin or Sir George Darwin, but early in 1919 Joseph Proudman of Liverpool University (see Chapter Fourteen) felt that the time had come for the formation of an Institute dedicated specifically to the subject of tides. He was a major influence in encouraging the Booth brothers, Charles Booth, Chairman of the Booth Steamship Company, and Sir Alfred Booth, Chairman of the Cunard Steamship Company, to provide funds for the foundation of the Liverpool Tidal Institute and

for its upkeep for a trial period of five years.
Additional grants were obtained from the British Association for the Advancement of Science and from the Department of Scientific and Industrial Research.

The Institute was situated in the George Holt Physics Laboratory at Liverpool University.

At the first meeting of the Tidal Institute Committee, Joseph Proudman was appointed as Honorary Director, with Dr. Arthur Doodson (see Chapter Fourteen) as Secretary.

Dr. Arthur Doodson
(Courtesy Proudman Oceanographic Laboratory)

In the same year, 1919, Joseph Proudman was appointed Professor of Applied Mathematics at Liverpool University. His salary immediately rose from £150 to £800 per annum. In 1920 it was increased to £1000 and remained at that figure for the next 23 years! This is not as bad as it sounds as prices either fell or showed only small increases in the 1920s and 1930s.

Professor Proudman was elected to the Royal Astronomical Society on 11th June 1920.

The objectives of the Tidal Institute were:-
1 To prosecute continuously scientific research into all aspects of knowledge of the tides.
2. To form a training school of applied mathematical research.
3. To form a bureau of organised information concerning the tides.
4. To undertake special pieces of tidal research for commercial or other bodies.

Professor Proudman was kept busy with his University commitments, and Dr. Doodson was largely responsible for the day-to-day running of the Tidal Institute. The Institute was allocated a room in Bidston Observatory, where research into tides was becoming increasingly important, so Dr. Doodson must have done a fair amount of commuting between Liverpool and Bidston. His salary, £350 per annum, was increased to £500 from 1st September 1920. His first assistant, Miss A.L.Cooper, B.Sc. had been a member of his staff at University College, London. She did analytical work at the University site and her salary was £100 per year.

Among the tidal records analysed were the observations made by Sir George Darwin in 1901 -1904 whilst exploring the Antarctic on the sailing ships Discovery and Scotia, together with those records sent to the Institute by the Australasian Antarctic expedition 1911 - 1914, led by Sir Douglas Mawson. Other observations came from the Cape Antarctic Expedition and the Gold Coast Survey. In 1924 data which had been recorded by the National Antarctic Expedition, led by Captain R.N. Scott, were analysed at the Institute.

Miss Cooper was later joined by Miss S.K.Lowry, at a salary of £100 per annum, and their lives were made slightly easier by the purchase of two calculating machines. The staff of the Tidal Institute now comprised four people – Professor Proudman, Dr. Doodson, Miss Cooper and Miss Lowry.

One of Dr. Doodson's many projects at this time was research into seiches on Lake Geneva. The results were published in 1920.

In those early years the Liverpool Tidal Institute relied very much on donations, mainly from the shipping world, and on grants. For example, in 1921 it received a grant of £600 from the DSCI (Department of Science and Industry). Salaries accounted for the major part of the expenditure.

In 1921 Professor Proudman wrote an account of the current state of tidal knowledge for publication in the Encyclopaedia Britannica. The following year he was a British delegate to the first Assembly of the International Union of Geodesy and Geophysics meeting in Rome, and was appointed its Secretary on the Committee on Tides. In 1923 he was awarded the Adams Prize - £234 - by the University of Cambridge for an essay on tides. He donated the money to the Liverpool

Tidal Institute "to be used to provide a tide gauge at Alfred Pierhead (where there is already a well for a tide gauge) activated electrically via the Time Gun."

Initially the Tidal Institute was governed by a committee nominated by the Council of the University, but from July 1st 1923 this was replaced by a joint committee of the University and the Mersey Docks and Harbour Board, in order to facilitate co-operation. Members of the committee included the Vice-Chancellor of the University, the President of the University Council, the Booth brothers, Mr. Plummer and Professor Proudman, with Dr. Doodson as the Secretary.

From 1923 work at the Institute continued to be financed by the Booth Shipping Companies in the form of the Booth Sustentation Fund and by the Liverpool Steamship Owners Association, together with a generous donation from the Moss Steamship Company and another substantial grant of £600 from the Department of Science and Industry. However finance was now beginning to come in from the sale of tidal information to various ports, and from commercial projects.

Back in 1872, the first tide predicting machine had been constructed by J. White of Glasgow to the design of Sir William Thomson, the future Lord Kelvin, but it had few mechanical components and consequently the resulting predictions were not very reliable. The machine was composed of "eight pulleys carried on axis at the ends of eight cranks of adjustable length, four on the upper side and four on the lower side of a wooden frame. A cord fixed at one end passed alternately under and over the lower and upper pulleys. Counterpoise weights were attached to the arms in the upper row. The centre of each pulley thus described a circle of adjustable radius, which circular motion was equivalent to the sum of two simple harmonic motions, one vertical and the other horizontal. Thus the hanging weight described the required complex motion."

The pulleys represented the various contributions to the tide resulting from the position of the Earth in relation to the sun and moon, the profile of the coast around the port in question, etc. If a predicting machine had only a few pulleys, then only a few aspects of the tide experienced at any particular port could be reproduced, and the resulting tidal predictions would be less accurate than they might otherwise have been. A second machine was produced in 1873 by A. Légé & Co. of Barnsbury St., London under the supervision of E. Roberts, at the request of the Tidal Committee of the British Association. This machine had ten components. Sir William Thomas was responsible for another improved model in 1875, while in 1879 Légé & Co. built a 20-24 component machine for sale to the Indian Authorities. In 1908 Légé & Co. built a 40-component machine for E. Roberts.

At Bidston, the Tidal Institute's first predictions - times and heights of high water at Liverpool for 1924 - were produced in 1923, under the supervision of Dr. Doodson, for publication in Holden's Tide Tables. This proved a very long exercise lasting about four days, using calculating machines. However it brought in a welcome £100 from Holdens. The following year times and heights of both high and low waters were predicted for Liverpool. A faster method of prediction was desirable.

Liverpool shipowners again came up trumps by donating most of the £1500 required to purchase a tide predicting machine and the British Association contributed £300. In 1924 the money was used to purchase a 26-component machine from Kelvin, Bottomley and Baird of Glasgow, with modifications suggested by Dr. Doodson (see Chapter Seventeen). This instrument was installed at Bidston, where a second room had been placed at the service of the Tidal Institute for the purpose of computation of tides.

The Institute's tidal predictions featured in the Hydrographic Department's Admiralty Tide Tables for the first time in 1925 when high and low waters for Liverpool were published. As time went on the Institute took on an increasing amount of tidal prediction work including seven Australian and New Zealand ports and three Japanese ports.

In 1924 the Electrical Engineer to the Borough of Birkenhead was instructed to lay an electricity cable to the Observatory at an expense estimated at £50, and by June 1925 electricity had been installed in the dwelling house and the Observatory at a cost of £66. The electricity bill (paid to the Corporation of Birkenhead) averaged £2-7-9d per month.

Income from the testing of chronometers, etc. was modest: - £15-13-3 in 1926, while payments received from the sale of meteorological data amounted to a total of £19-0-0 for the year. Gun maintenance cost an average £100 per annum.

Salaries of Observatory staff in 1926 were as follows:-
The Director   -   £750 per annum
Senior lady assistant   -   £235 per annum
Second lady assistant   -   £145 per annum
Junior assistant   -   £70 per annum
(There is no mention of Mr. Skinner's salary)

The Doodsons' first child, Joan, was born in the early months of 1927. At that time the Doodsons are believed to have lived in the Sefton Park area of Liverpool.

Meanwhile Plummer, now in his mid seventies, remained in residence at Bidston as the Director of the Observatory. His wife Sarah passed away in the summer of 1927 at the age of 77. They had been married for 56 years. Plummer concentrated on his great love of astronomy and on the meteorological work. The telescopes were still in good order and the transit continued to be used in conjunction with Paris and Nordleich to determine time by the "wireless telegraphic apparatus." The one o'clock gun was firing well, and all three anemometers, the Robinson, the Osler and the Dines were still in use.

In 1926 the amount of analysis work was "greatly" extended. Analysis, in its simplest form, is the reverse of tidal prediction. A series of tidal observations from a port is split up into the components of the tide (effects of sun, moon, profile of the area, etc), and information relating to time and date is removed. The resulting values can then be used to predict future tides at the port. The number of British Port Authorities requesting tidal predictions steadily increased and major work was undertaken for the Canadian Hydrographic Office.

A total eclipse of the sun was viewed in England in 1927. It is reported that 50,000 people assembled on Bidston Hill to observe the event.

Plummer's health began to decline, and early in 1927 his assistant, Mr.Skinner, died at the age of 67. Mr. Skinner had been the senior assistant at the Observatory since the time of John Hartnup Junior, yet we have very little information about him or how he died. His death seems have been unexpected though, because Norman C. Hobbs, a junior assistant at the Observatory, was paid a bonus of £5 for the extra duties undertaken due to Plummer's illness and before a new assistant could be appointed. The following timetable of duties was presumably drawn up by Mr. Plummer and issued as a job description for Mr. Skinner's successor:-

"MARINE SURVEYOR AND WATER BAILLIFF'S DEPARTMENT – April 11th 1927
 ASSISTANT TO DIRECTOR OF BIDSTON OBSERVATORY.
CONDITIONS OF SERVICE, DUTIES, etc.
1. Assistant responsible to Director.
2. No accommodation provided.
3. Provide own food.
4. Twelve working days leave, with pay, allowed annually, at such time as convenient to the work of the Observatory - Bank Holidays at the discretion of the Director.
5. Under Pension Insurance Scheme - Assistant pays one third and Observatory Joint Committee two thirds.

6. Compulsory retirement at the age of 65 years.

7. Engagement terminable by one month's notice in writing from either side.

8. Hours of duty - every day including Sundays and Bank Holidays, at the discretion of the Director.

DAILY ROUTINE
TIME: G.M.T.
A.M.

7.0	Met Telegram to Air Ministry.
7.15	Change and develop seismograph records.
7.55	Take Paris Time Signal and Air Ministry Report.
8.15	Draw chart. Receive Wireless Report. Readings (Tidal Institute).
9.0	Dock Board Telegram. Change Barograph.
9.15	Change Thermograph. Write up hourly readings.
9.30	Take Greenwich Mean Time on wireless.
10.0	Change Anemograph.
10.30	Time Signal.
11.0	Error of Lancaster clock taken.
11.5	Give gunner time.
Noon:	Read Barometer and Thermometer. Gun signal.

P.M.

12.30	Sidereal Clocks compared and reduced.
12.55	Gun.
1.0:	Telephone Air Ministry Readings.
3.0	Take and record meteorological observations.
6.05	Telephone telegram to Air Ministry.
7.15	Work for Tidal Institute.
9.0	Take readings: enter in Air Ministry Book.

Daily Report to "Daily Post."
At sunset change sun card on roof and tabulate amount (of sunshine).

SPECIAL WORK

MONDAY: Fill in forms for (3) Medical Officers and Tramway Office, Liverpool.

THURSDAY: Wind Lancaster Clock.

FRIDAY: Wind Dines and Anemometer.

SATURDAY: Begin to fill in graphs to be finished later.
             Post Met weekly result sheet to General Manager.
             Post Weather Curve to Marine Surveyor.
             Post Mean Time clock error for week.

SUNDAY: Post Barometric curve for week ending midnight on Saturday, to Engineer, Dock Office.
             Post weekly card to Meteorological Office.
             Wind barograph.

DAILY: GENERAL OFFICE WORK.
             Correspondence.
             Prepare any statistics that may be required.

(This refers to any general recording or anything that may be required by any authorised Authority).
Examine sextants, thermometers and rate chronometers.

This gives us an interesting insight into the strict Observatory routine in operation at that time. The post was taken up by Herbert James Bigelstone, at a salary of £250 per annum. He had served with the Royal Flying Corps in the 1914-18 war, and he remained at Bidston for nearly 22 years.

Mr. Plummer's health continued to fail and he died on May 22nd 1928, at the age of 79, from a "painful spinal complaint." The funeral service was conducted by the vicar, assisted by Rev. Eric Robson. Mr Plummer's grave can be seen in Bidston churchyard.

Rev. Robson kept detailed weather records at his home in West Kirby in the early years of the Century, and, following his own death, these records were donated to the Observatory by his family.

Mr. Bigelstone was invited to take up residence at the Observatory, but he turned down the offer as he was planning to marry. Presumably his future wife did not fancy the idea of living in a draughty old building.

Two young ladies, Ada Ainsworth and Dorothy Dodd, both aged 16, joined the staff that year. They worked 9-30 am to 4-30 pm each day, and 9-30 am till 12 noon on alternate Saturdays.

In January 1928 disastrous flooding occurred in the Thames, causing the deaths of fourteen people in London. The Tidal Institute, at the request of London County Council and the Port of London Authority, immediately appointed a committee to consider the problems. A report was presented to Parliament in March, recommending that the Tidal Institute should examine certain scientific questions in co-operation with the Hydrographic Department of the Admiralty and the Meteorological Office. Dr. Doodson submitted a scheme for a preliminary investigation and was told to go ahead.

He "immediately made a vigorous attack on the problems" and presented a report at the end of May. He studied the storm effects hour by hour of four great storms and the associated variation of sea levels all around the North Sea, using records from London Bridge, Southend, Felixstowe, Dunbar, and information from Belgium, Holland, Germany and Denmark.

Mr. Plummer's death seems to have paved the way for major changes, for in 1929 the University's Tidal Institute was moved over to Bidston and amalgamated with the Observatory to form the Liverpool Observatory and Tidal Institute (LOTI). This was done so that "the facilities which the Observatory and the Tidal Institute afford for the advancement of knowledge and diffusion of science and learning may be extended and increased." Professor Proudman became Honorary Director, whilst continuing his duties at the University. He received an honorarium of £250 per annum for his Bidston responsibilities. Dr. Doodson was appointed Associate Director of Bidston at a salary of £850 per annum. He was responsible for the day-to-day running of the Institute, and he opted to take up residence at the Observatory with his family. In return for free accommodation with rates, taxes, coal and lighting all paid for, he was required to keep the gardens, lawns and walks in good order. Trees and ornamental shrubs were to be properly pruned, and no trees or shrubs were to be cut down or removed without the consent in writing of the Dock Board.

A sample of the Observatory's Income and Expenditure account in those days shows that in the year 1929 income amounted to £3705 and expenditure was £3558.

In June 1929 Mr. H. W. T. Roberts of Messrs E. Roberts and Sons of Broadstairs passed away suddenly and his firm of tidal and astronomical computer makers ceased to operate. Mr. Roberts had not completed his programme of tidal predictions, so there was pressure on L.O.T.I. to fill the gap. L.O.T.I. was offered the Légé tide predicting machine, designed by Lord Kelvin and Mr. Roberts and built by A. Légé and Company of London in 1906, and the offer was accepted. The price paid was £753-15-0d.[3] The machine had 33 mechanical components, but Dr. Doodson made improvements to it, extending the number of components to 40. At Bidston Observatory the Roberts was housed in a different room from the Kelvin machine, and it remained in use till 1960.

A new, updated, Dines anemometer was also installed in 1929, on the recommendation of Dr. Simpson, Director of the Meteorological Office, as the old instrument was suspect. Weather reports were sent to the Meteorological Office at 7a.m., 1p.m. and 6p.m. daily.

A new appointee to the staff in 1929 was Robert Henry Corkan. He had been born in Sulby on the Isle of Man in 1906. Following his father's appointment as station master at Port St. Mary, Henry attended Port St. Mary Boys' School, and moved on to Douglas Secondary School in 1918. In 1925 he became a student in the Department of Applied Mathematics at Liverpool University under Professor Proudman

Robert Henry Corkan
(Courtesy Proudman Oceanographic Laboratory)

and obtained his B.Sc. honours degree in mathematics in 1927. He was planning to study for a teacher's certificate, but when Professor Proudman recommended him for a post at the newly formed L.O.T.I. in January 1929, he felt it was an opportunity not to be missed. He took up the post at a starting salary of £250 per annum, and he worked closely with Dr. Doodson on tidal research.

On the domestic side it seems that prior to 1930 the only water supply to the Observatory premises was in the living accommodation, for a memo sent to the Dock Board from Professor Proudman that year asked if a ladies' toilet might be installed, as otherwise the Doodsons could not close up their home when away. (Gentlemen presumably used the privy in the courtyard). Also the charwomen had to get their water from the house as "water did not extend to the Observatory itself." The toilet would cost £162 and a housemaid's sink would be £6.

The reply is not recorded, but it is to be hoped that the Dock Board acceded to the request.

In 1930 the Royal Society ran a competition to find the best contribution to improvements in the science and practice of navigation. There were twenty entries and Dr. Doodson won the £250 prize for his work on the analysis and prediction of tidal currents.

As the Great Depression began to bite around 1931, the Dock Board, in common with many other companies, found it necessary to implement salary cuts of up to 10% for all grades.

The Doodsons' second child, Thomas, was born on the Observatory premises on March 6th 1931, but his mother, Margaret, died, at the early age of 41, possibly from appendicitis, only two weeks after his birth. A Church member, Elsie Mary Carey, looked after the children, and two years later she became Dr. Doodson's second wife. Local press reports of the wedding make interesting reading:-

"The wedding took place at the Atherton Mission Hall, Exmouth Street, (Charing Cross), Birkenhead, on Wednesday. Dr. Doodson was Associate Director of the Observatory at the time. The ceremony was performed by Mr. J. Miller of Ayr, and was attended by several prominent scientists and the members of the Observatory staff. The bride was escorted by Mr. Ernest Doodson, the bridegroom's brother. She was wearing a simply cut gown of new-rose embossed velvet with touches of white at the neck and wrists. Her hat of French velours matched her dress, and rose and white chrysanthemum blooms were mingled with sprays of white heather in her bouquet. She was attended by two seven-year-olds, Joan Doodson, daughter of the bridegroom, and Noreen Doodson, his niece. Over their pretty knee length frocks of ivory lisse they had long "Red Riding Hood" capes of pastel blue velvet, and their caps of white ruched English net were tied with satin ribbons at one side. They carried silver baskets of tulips and white hyacinths.

The bridegroom was accompanied by Mr. and Mrs. Martin of Wigan. At the reception at Atherton Hall, the bridegroom's mother, Mrs. Doodson, acted as hostess. She was wearing a gracefully draped gown of black marocain with a hat en suite. Mrs. Ernest Doodson, who assisted to receive, came in a smart navy eponge ensemble with accessories to accord. Among the guests was Mrs. Manley, the bride's sister. The couple are spending their honeymoon in Edinburgh, and the bride travelled in a twine beige tailleur frock and rose velour hat with a grey squirrel coat - the gift of the bridegroom."

Another press report gives further details:-
"The wedding was the first to be solemnised at Atherton Hall, and was attended by members of the community of the Church of God from many outlying districts including Blackburn, Wigan, St. Helens, Southport, and Barrow. The simple service included readings from Old and New Testaments, the hymns "O God to Thee our voice we lift" and "Gracious Father, God of Love", and the Doxology, sung unaccompanied.
The bride wore a becoming gown of deep ruby-red faconne velvet, designed on simple lines, with a gilet shell-pink egeorgette which also bordered the neckline. The moulded corsage merged into a long skirt falling in graceful folds to her oyster-satin slippers.
The reception was for over 140 guests.
The honeymoon will be spent on a motor tour of Edinburgh and Southern Scotland."

In the same year Dr. Doodson was appointed a Fellow of the Royal Society. At this time the staff of the L.O.T.I. numbered nine: Professor Proudman and Mrs A. Leslie Dennis were located at the University, while the seven at Bidston were Dr. Doodson, H. J. Bigelstone, Henry Corkan, Ada Ainsworth, Dorothy Dodd, George Kirkland and Joan Stott. Henry Corkan worked on tides and was awarded an M.Sc. by the

University of Liverpool in July 1933 for a thesis describing his research. The following year he married Dorothy Dodd, who, as the wife of a scientist employed at the Observatory, was required, by convention, to resign her post.

Mr. Bigelstone instructs a "computer" in the use of the Kelvin tidal prediction machine sometime in the 1930s.

(Courtesy Proudman Oceanographic Laboratory)

In the same year Professor Proudman was appointed to the Chair of Oceanography at Liverpool University, following the death of Professor James Johnstone.

Dr. Doodson's daughter Joan later developed a tumour on her leg. In those days there was no effective cure, and sadly she died on April 26th 1936 aged only nine. These must have been traumatic years for Dr. Doodson, losing his first wife in 1931, re-marrying and then losing his daughter in 1936.

Thomas Doodson was educated at Birkenhead School, and then sailed as a midshipman with the Blue Funnel Line of Alfred Holt and Company.

Pay restraint was eased after a few years. A memo of December 18th 1935 shows a generous increase in wage for Margaret Gill, a recent appointee to the staff, from 20/- to 25/- a week, and one on December 23rd 1936 shows an even better rise for Ruby C. Roberts and Marjorie Robinson, also recent recruits, - an increase from 20/- to 30/- per week. Would anyone turn down a 50% increase in pay?

(Courtesy Miss A. Corkan)
The above photo was taken about 1936 and shows -Dr. Doodson, Mrs. Dorothy Corkan, Mrs. Elsie Doodson, George Kirkland? and Henry Corkan

Holiday allowances seem to have been generous for those days. All staff were on 24 working days leave from January 1936, apart from the Associate Director, Dr. Doodson, and Miss Cooper - their leave was left to the discretion of the

Director. Perhaps it should be born in mind that all staff were on a five and a half day working week at that time.

A new recruit to the staff at Bidston in 1937 was John Reginald Rossiter. He had been born in September 1919, and gained a scholarship to the Liverpool Collegiate College, where he obtained his Higher School Certificate. He was keen on sport, playing in the First Eleven Football side, and he was a Senior Prefect. His parents wanted him to move on to University, but finance was tight and he had other plans. Unbeknown to his family, he applied for a post at L.O.T.I. at Bidston. He was successful at the interview and was taken on as a junior technical assistant, commuting by bicycle from his home in Liverpool. His salary was £80 per annum, and he worked on the prediction and analysis of tides. His painstaking and conscientious attitude to work was soon apparent. That same year Miss Joan Duckworth was taken on as a 16 year old assistant. Another romance was about to blossom! Her salary was, like that of other girls starting work at the Observatory, £1 per week.

Margaret Gill was Henry Corkan's assistant. He continued his research work into tides, recorded both in the sea and on land. Seismographs, located in the vault below the basement, continued to record earth movements. In a press interview on Nov. 21st 1937 Mr. Corkan said: "Near every coast the ground is actually and ruthlessly bent downwards by the load of sea water thrown upon the earth's edge as high tide is being reached. In Liverpool Bay, for example, at every high tide, the extra weight of water makes the Wirral Peninsula and all there is on it, bow gracefully to the north, its normal level being gradually restored as the tide recedes."

Dr. S. F. Grace was a lecturer in applied mathematics at Liverpool University at this time. Although not a member of the Observatory staff, he frequently spent time at Bidston over a period of six years and did much valuable research on tides, particularly those in the Bristol and English Channels. He published many papers on the subject. Pages and pages of his research work, consisting of columns of incredibly neat handwritten figures, are still to be found in the Bidston archives. Unfortunately he died in 1937, having never completely recovered from wounds suffered in the Great War.

In 1938 Professor Proudman was invited to be guest of honour at the annual prize-giving of the Douglas High School for Boys and Girls, held in Villa Marina in the Isle of Man. In his speech he paid tribute to Henry Corkan, old boy of the school. His words were - "About nine years ago I had the task of filling a vacancy which had arisen on the staff of the Tidal Institute. I chose Mr. Corkan, and the choice has been a very fortunate one, because he has shown, not only the qualities I wanted, but also qualities which at that time I had no right to expect. Mr. Corkan is a very reliable officer and a very competent man of science, and I congratulate the school on producing him."[4]

Professor Proudman and Dr. Doodson made numerous visits overseas in the 1920s and 1930s. Destinations included Canada and the USA and many venues in Europe. However all such activity was to cease with the outbreak of the Second World War.

Chapter Ten

World War II

On June 30th 1939 Dr. Doodson planned to combine holiday with work by sailing across the Atlantic on board the Duchess of York, accompanied by his second wife and son Thomas (now aged 8), in order to enjoy a touring holiday before attending a conference in Washington.[1] They visited Seattle and the Grand Canyon. Dr. Doodson then attended a meteorological conference in Toronto and visited the Hydrographic Service in Ottawa. Together with Professor Proudman he was planning to attend an assembly of the International Union of Geodesy and Geophysics in Washington in early September. At the conference Dr. Doodson was to give two lectures, one describing deep sea pressure gauge experiments for recording tides, the other describing the electrically recording current-meter which he had designed himself and tested out on the Zephyr (see Chapter Nineteen). Professor Proudman was to lecture on the aims and results of the experiments.

They expected to be back in Britain on September 19th. However the outbreak of the Second World War brought the trip to a premature end. Dr. Doodson was recalled to Bidston, but presumably Professor Proudman continued with the itinerary. The journey home proved quite an adventure for the Doodson family. They came back on the Empress of Canada, escorted by six destroyers, sailing from Halifax to Liverpool. The crossing, which should have taken six days, actually took 19 days, as the convoy was diverted south almost to the Equator to avoid enemy submarines.

At the beginning of the war the Institute worked "all out" to get ahead with its normal work relating to the tides of 82 principal ports throughout the British Empire. The most urgent need was to advance the completion date of predictions; the normal date was brought forward by more than a year so that in the event of damage to the machines there would be opportunity for repair without causing serious inconvenience. Photographic equipment was obtained and apparatus made by the staff to obtain micro-films of the predictions, copies of which were kept in separate buildings at the Observatory and other copies were stored elsewhere in the country. Thus any predictions lost at sea could be easily replaced.

The publication of detailed data concerning British ports came to a halt on Nov. 15th 1940. Under Regulation 3 of the Defence (General) Regulations 1939, "It was prohibited, save with written authority first obtained from the Hydrographer of the Navy or a duly appointed official acting on his behalf, to publish any tidal predictions, hydrographic information or other port information heretofore published in part or in whole in the public press and also normally included in books and pamphlets issued in respect of facilities obtaining at British ports. Tidal, hydrographic and port information is useful to an enemy." In other words tidal information could no longer be published in almanacs, diaries or newspapers without prior permission. The well-known Browns' Almanac must have had such permission. A letter dated 7th April 1941 shows that Dr. Doodson, acting on Browns' behalf, requested and received permission from the New Zealand Government to substitute the 1942 tidal predictions for Auckland and Dunedin for those of two European ports (unnamed).

There was an embargo on making written reference to the war even in the meteorological diaries.
The only reference I have been able to find in them was at the height of the Blitz, on May 3rd 1941, when it was reported that "Misty conditions were accentuated by smoke from fires during the night."

Twice daily weather reports were sent to the Controller, A.R.P. (Air Raid Precautions) Headquarters Liverpool. (On December 7th 1944 the Controller gave permission for these to be discontinued).

Annual Reports of the Observatory activities were suspended 1940-44 but re-commenced with a 1940 -1945 summary after restrictions on publicity were relaxed.

Dr. Doodson was required to remain at his post, supervising the tidal predictions which were necessary for military use, but all his male staff and several of the women volunteered for, or were called up for, active service.

Mr. H. J. Bigelstone, the principal assistant, was seconded to serve as a Lieutenant-Commander, R.N.V.R. He served in the naval meteorological branch and was attached to Fleet Air Arm stations.

The Admiralty requested that Henry Corkan be seconded to the Nautical Almanac Office, located at that time in Bath, under the leadership of Commander W. I. Farquharson R.N., Commander Warburg's successor as Superintendent of Tidal Branch, where Mr. Corkan was to carry out special investigations into tides in the Far East. This was agreed on the understanding that he would be relinquished if Dr. Doodson became incapacitated or the tidal prediction machines were damaged by enemy action.

John Rossiter, having obtained his Intermediate B.Sc. in August 1939, was called up on January 14th 1940. Initially he served at Saighton Camp in Cheshire with the Royal Artillery. From 1940-1946 he was an Instructor in Anti-Aircraft Gunnery and a REME Education Officer serving at Brayton, Yorkshire.

Mrs. A. Leslie Dennis B.Sc. joined the WAAFs and Sybil Bray and Margaret Harriman, both recent appointees to the Bidston staff, were seconded to ATS signals as Corporals in 1942.

Margaret Harriman was one of six cipher operators attached to the Australian Army. During her secondment she worked in Australia House, London, for four months and deciphered messages to and from places such as Melbourne and Washington. Soon she was posted to Brussels where she worked in the cipher section of H/Q 21 Army Group Signals. She was later posted to Germany where she was stationed at Bad Oeyenhausen.

Amy Higson, who had joined the staff as an assistant in 1936, took on overall responsibility for the meteorological work with great success during the later war years while the men were on active service, and was commended in the 1946 annual report.

Margaret Gill was granted £200 per annum from 1st January 1945 plus an extra £25 whilst acting as assistant. "This was a pecuniary reward for her valuable work in acting as Principal Assistant to the Director (in the absence of H. J. Bigelstone) during the recent emergency." (The letter to her commends her 'zealous and able services'). She married in March 1945, to become Mrs. Harris, and resigned in 1946.

The onset of war had brought about considerable changes at Bidston. The one o'clock gun firing was discontinued from Sept. 2nd 1939.

Early contingency plans had proposed that in the event of war the Kelvin tide predicting machine, normally located in the main room which had a wooden floor, should be moved to No 8 cellar, the seismograph room, to reduce the risk of fire and damage.

The Roberts-Légé was to be moved to another building, the garage at the bottom of the garden, so that if one machine were lost due to enemy action, hopefully the other would remain intact. This outside

The garage at the bottom of the garden

garage room was half sunk below ground level on two sides (see photo) and was substantially protected by blast proof walls on the other sides. A strong roof was placed over it. (Back in the 19th century the lower end of this building had provided stabling for the Hartnups' horse.)

When hostilities began the plans were carried out, and neither machine suffered any damage, though the door of the garage was damaged by a bomb blast.

From time to time, as circumstances indicated the need, the main building was also protected, and none of the scientific equipment suffered the slightest degree of damage at any time.

Though the Observatory itself is somewhat isolated it is close to one of the most frequently damaged areas. The windows of the building were seriously affected on six occasions. Nearly a hundred panes of glass were shattered on the second occasion, and temporary covers were renewed several times thereafter. Doors suffered badly, and two interior walls and four ceilings were damaged. Much help was rendered by the dockyard staff from Birkenhead Docks, but most of the work of repair had to be done by the Observatory staff. Though many bombs and incendiaries fell just outside the grounds none fell inside.

Lord Haw-Haw (the name given by British people to William Joyce, who after the war was hanged for treason) - broadcasting from Hamburg - is reputed to have said "By morning Bidston Observatory will be no more." This report came from Dr. Doodson, and implies that the Nazi hierarchy was well aware of Bidston's involvement in the war effort. William Joyce had close connections with Wirral. Fortunately his threat was to be proved erroneous.

The Doodsons took shelter in the cellars at night during the war. Some damage was suffered from 1940 onwards. In a letter to Commander Warburg of the Hydrographic Office, dated March 6th 1941, Dr. Doodson commented that there had been "quiet conditions here for a while, though four or five bombs were dropped on the open hill last week without any damage. They were not quite so near as those which blew out our windows last Christmas."
However, a few weeks later, in the Blitz of May 1941 Liverpool was one of the most heavily bombed cities in the country, second only to London, a total of 4200 people being killed.

In November 1941 numerous members of the public reported that flashing lights were being signalled to German planes. Mr. J. C. Evans of Oxton, a Sergeant in the Intelligence Corps, stationed at Western Command H/Q, was instructed to keep watch from the Observatory for these flashing lights for a period of seven nights. He was able to plot every light he saw and provide an explanation for them. It was concluded that the explanation was the flashing of hooded car headlights on to shop windows.

The damaged windows in the observatory were not replaced until 1946. The cost was £146. The late Thomas Doodson told me how, in the meantime, his father hit upon the idea of replacing the windows with celluloid mesh, spread over wire frames. The frames were on springs so that in the event of future bomb blasts, they would spring out of position and then back again without much damage being caused.

The residents of the cottages had Anderson shelters to protect them during the air raids. The young people sat there drinking hot cocoa, as they watched the invading planes fly over Liverpool. They saw fires spring up as the bombs struck their targets.

A resident of the cottages told how one night while Dr. Doodson was firewatching on the roof, Mr. McClusker, husband of a cleaner at the Observatory, was on duty with a colleague by the water fountain, just beyond the southern boundary wall of the Observatory. They saw a parachute coming down, and, believing it to be a man, went to meet it. Unfortunately it was a landmine, and both Mr. McClusker and his colleague were killed. The explosion blew out many windows in the Observatory, but the instruments were unharmed. Another landmine fell close to the windmill, and a third one hit the garden nurseries on the hill. Greenhouses in the area were badly hit - it was believed that enemy aircraft pilots mistook their glint for water, and thought they were bombing the docks.
There is a story that a child lost a limb at that time. Another story, possibly referring to the same incident, says that a child put his foot on a bomb on the hill and was killed.

During the air raids, in addition to their daytime duties, four female members of staff were on the firewatch rota, each staying on the premises one or two nights per week (all the men, apart from Dr. Doodson, being away in the forces). In 1942 those involved were Joan Duckworth, Estelle Gilbert, Amy Higson and Dorothy Webster. A total of eight people were needed to form the fire-watching team, so Dr. Doodson and a few friends completed the number. The use of staff as firewatchers was approved by the Fire Officer for Birkenhead.

The women wore tin helmets and trenchcoats while on duty, and buckets of sand, long-handled shovels and pumps were available to extinguish any incendiary bombs. Joan Rossiter (née Duckworth) says that she was never actually required to douse a fire on the roof, although she recalls being on fire-watch with a colleague during one of the heaviest incendiary attacks of the Blitz. The girls were very frightened as bombs fell all over the hill, and as time went on they withdrew further and further down the staircase.

Between summonses from the air raid sirens they were allowed to sleep in one of the two libraries that existed at that time.

Some interesting correspondence survives:-
In a letter to the Mersey Docks and Harbour Board, Dr.Doodson inquired if bedding should be provided for the firewatchers. The Secretary replied to the effect that "the obligation placed upon employers as regards Fire Watchers was that sleeping accommodation should be provided. A 'good employer' would doubtless construe this as providing sheets, but it could not be regarded as an absolute obligation." He therefore proposed to seek approval from the Chairman of

the Board before agreeing to the purchase. In the meantime he asked for estimated costs, so the next day Dr. Doodson made some enquiries. Robbs Ltd. of Birkenhead, could not supply more than one pair of sheets without a priority order from the Board of Trade. Prices were from 30/- to 33/6 per pair. Allanson's Ltd. also of Birkenhead, didn't mention priority orders, but quoted 32/6 per pair (unbleached), 37/6 (only six pairs in stock) or 40/- per pair (bleached). Dr. Doodson reckoned that, if each of the firewatchers was provided with a pair of sheets, and these were laundered once a month, (i.e. two pairs in the wash each week), then ten pairs of sheets would be required, bringing the total purchase price up to £20. No follow-up correspondence survives, but Joan Rossiter cannot recall that sheets were ever provided, although they did have camp beds and blankets. Presumably the Chairman of the Dock Board decided the cost of sheets was prohibitive.

REPORT ON FIRE RISKS AND SECURITY -
(Dr. Doodson's memo - 27th July 1942)
(a) Each member of staff performs the duty once per week, and on a weeknight stays on after normal office hours to do two hours' overtime followed by firewatching. The assistant therefore has stayed on the premises from early morning one day until afternoon of the following day.
(b) No assistant normally stays overnight on Saturday, but works on Saturday afternoon once in six weeks so as to leave at least one person in the building. The time so spent is allowed off at some other time.
(c) Each assistant in turn works all day Sunday and continues overnight on firewatching duties. This arrangement is

preferred to any other that has been proposed.

(d) Extra payments have been made as follows:-

    Overtime (two hours per week at 1/- per hour)   : 2/-

    Sunday work (6.5 hours every 6th week)   : 7/6

These were understood to be comparable with Dock Board rates.

Firewatching allowances: 4/6 per night, but recently reduced to 3/- per night.

PROPOSED CHANGES

(1) Changes in hours cannot be made as it is necessary for someone to be on duty on Saturday afternoon and on Sunday for normal observatory duties and also for reports to ARP authorities. The pressure of work has been so great that it has been necessary on frequent occasions to have extra people in on Saturdays and Sundays.

(2) The allowances for overtime are too small. The average rate of payment for normal hours is about 1/6 per hour, and I propose that the rates be as follows:

Overtime   : 2/- per hour.

Sunday work   : 12/6 per day.

(3) The security measures in lieu of firewatching will require payment, and it is proposed to pay 4/- per night, as the assistant is not able to leave and return to the premises after normal business hours, particularly in winter.

Members of staff were paid a war grant, approximately 10% of salary, which was merged with salary.

At the end of 1942 Dock Board staff were given an extra cash payment to cover overtime work during the war. The female staff at Bidston heard of this and asked for a similar payment and were successful. They were given 7.5% of annual salary. This payment continued in subsequent years.

Dr. Doodson requested an increased petrol ration while Corkan and Rossiter were away, on the grounds that, if he could drive to appointments rather than rely on public transport, his absences from the Observatory could be kept to a minimum. This was desirable as his all female staff would be alone at such times. He was advised to apply to the Petroleum Officer in Manchester. (There is no record of the outcome).

It is interesting to note that correspondence to the LOTI Chairman, Colonel Beazley, normally addressed to the M.D.H.B. Liverpool, was sent to St. Saviour's Parish Hall, Oxton, from July 1941. This was probably a precautionary move to safer premises, as the Liverpool H/Q had suffered some bomb damage in the May Blitz.

Despite the bomb damage at Bidston, work continued without interruption; long hours were worked and arrangements made for keeping the machines running from early morning till late at night seven days a week.

As the War continued, more countries became involved, and providing tidal predictions for their ports meant an increasing workload for Bidston, as did naval and military needs. In a later press interview Dr. Doodson said: "Very great demands have been and are being made on the Institute. Often there will be an urgent call for predictions, which means that a big assignment already on one of the machines has to be removed and replaced by the 'first priority' one. Then the original assignment can be put back. The demand may be 'at once' or 'as soon as possible', and the work is tackled without delay at any time of day or night. I should like to bear testimony to the loyalty of my staff in getting out this work as quickly as possible. They work late hours on Saturdays and Sundays and they spare no effort to produce what is required."

Most notably, Dr. Doodson and his staff of six girls, already working overtime, were called upon, at short notice, in 1944 to prepare tide tables for various locations along the coast of Northern France. The routine predictions, already set up on the machines, as usual had to be quickly dismantled and the emergency ones installed. These emergency predictions were used for the D-Day landings on June 6th.

Speaking of the tidal predictions prepared for the D-Day landings in a press interview Dr. Doodson said: "The place was quite unknown to us then, but we now know that it was the place at which the invading forces actually landed." He stressed the point that there was no question of the Institute's being consulted as to where the invasion should take place. He added - "In all such instances (and there have been many) in which tidal predictions were requested, the names of the localities were concealed by numbers or codes, and my staff did not know, or desire to know, any more on that head. What they did welcome, however, was tidal information on which, or on their deductions from which, they could by various means build up a reliable prediction of what would happen at any given hour."

Professor Proudman was heavily involved in the administration of Liverpool University during the war years. From 1940 to 1946 he was Pro-Vice-Chancellor and Deputy Chairman of Senate.

At that stage Bidston was the foremost tidal predicting station in the world. The Coast and Geodetic Survey of the United States came second, but at that time was producing one third the quantity of predictions that Bidston produced.

In those days it was customary for ladies to cease working when they married. A revealing memo survives from 9th October 1944:

'Although not recorded in the minutes, the Observatory Committee agreed that Dr. Doodson might inform those female members of his staff who were married, that in all probability their services would be retained for 12 months after conclusion of hostilities, but that no guarantee of permanent employment could be given'.

Meanwhile Henry Corkan continued his work for the Admiralty. In 1945 it was intended that he should travel abroad, probably to the Far East, to further his work. A letter which he wrote to Dr. Doodson, from Bath, dated 15th April that year, shows that he had just been to London for "further innoculations", and was due to sail on the first available passage after April 30th. He was given the honorary appointment of a Naval Lieutenant Commander, and issued with uniform. Then, if he had the misfortune to fall into enemy hands, he would be treated as a military prisoner rather than risk being shot as a civilian. However he was soon back at Bidston, so the trip was presumably cancelled owing to the cessation of war.

John Rossiter married Joan Duckworth in May 1945, and was demobilized in May 1946. He planned to use his statutory 56 days leave allowance in studying for his Degree. However, Dr. Doodson was so short staffed that he persuaded him to work at Bidston in the mornings and study in the afternoons. For this Rossiter was paid an extra £3 per week. He continued to study in his free time and was awarded a London External Degree of B.Sc. Honours (1st class) in 1947.

In a testimonial sent from the Militia Camp at Brayton, Major S.J.Smith said:

"Sergeant Rossiter has been a member of this company for a considerable period and has always carried out his duties most conscientiously. His work has been thorough and painstaking and he has an excellent record as an army tradesman. It was however when the Army Education Scheme was implemented that Sergeant Rossiter proved himself invaluable. He showed great powers of organisation and co-ordination and also distinguished himself as an instructor in various classes. It is to him that the Education Scheme of this Company owes much of its success. He can be thoroughly recommended to any employer as a man who is keenly interested in his work and who spares no effort in whatever job he undertakes."

These qualities were to prove a great asset to John Rossiter in future years.

Chapter Eleven

Bidston Observatory: Postwar

Dr. Doodson seems to have had some difficulty in retaining young staff in the immediate post war years.

On Sept 11th 1945 one female recruit expressed a wish to pursue a London B.Sc. external degree. However Dr. Doodson pointed out: "Such high qualifications were not essential for the job and therefore Bidston could not be expected to grant facilities or pay expenses." He felt the Observatory Committee would most likely be sympathetic towards her desire, and no doubt would in some way or other take account of her new qualification in future if any of the senior girls left a vacancy. Professor Proudman agreed that she could have an unpaid day off for practical laboratory work in chemistry and physics (it is not clear whether this was to be weekly or just a one-off), and he would like to retain her services. However on Oct 6th, only three weeks later, she terminated her services at LOTI and went to work for D. Napier and Son, Ltd., Presumably they were more amenable to her wishes.

Mrs. A. Lesley Dennis was demobilized from the WAAFs in 1946, and was free to return to her duties at the Observatory following the mandatory 56 days leave for forces discharged from the services. However, she decided that her eyes could no longer take the strain of the close work required by Bidston, and this, combined with the fact that she now lived in Chester and would find the journey lengthy, and was already finding postwar housekeeping a strain, prompted her to tender her resignation.

In 1946 the Roberts-Légé tide predictor was moved back to the observatory basement and the opportunity was taken to give the machine a thorough overhaul. The partition wall separating the east and west libraries was removed, and the principal room and maid's bedroom were re-decorated at a cost of £50 for the two.

Due to other commitments Professor Proudman resigned from the Directorship of the Observatory in December 1945 at the age of 57, and Dr. Doodson replaced him.

Following the war, analysis of data, prediction of tides and the design of tide prediction machines for overseas clients, became a leading activity at Bidston.

Henry Corkan researched the conditions which cause storm surges in the Thames Estuary, and devised formulae which could forecast, from a knowledge of the meteorological conditions, the danger of imminent storm surges, with a good degree of accuracy. This was a continuation of the work done by Dr. Doodson following the North Sea storm surge and resulting Thames floods of 1928.

Henry Corkan was a member of a party which, in 1946, utilised a disused anti-aircraft (AA) fort in Liverpool Bay in order to continue Dr. Doodson's study of deep sea turbulence (see Chapter Nineteen). Three AA forts had been set up in Liverpool Bay on government orders in 1942 in an attempt to break up enemy bomber formations as they approached Liverpool from the seaward side. After the war the forts fell into disuse, but Henry Corkan's group realised that deep sea observations made from a platform with a firm foundation would give advantages over those made from a ship. Permission was obtained from the General Officer Commanding, Anti-Aircraft Command, for Bidston to use one of the disused forts. Corkan worked on the project in close co-operation with Wilfred Smith of Liverpool University's School of Geography. After some teething troubles, a Dines anemometer was erected on the fort, and the resulting analogue charts, which presumably had to be changed daily, were taken to Bidston for comparison with Bidston's wind records. Only two Royal Artillery engineers were stationed on the fort at any one time, and problems arising with the anemometer could not always be resolved. Consequently there were many gaps in the records. However several tables of comparisons are still stored in the Bidston archive. Henry Corkan was unable to obtain a firm response from the military authorities as to how long the fort might be available for Bidston's use. In the event the forts were dismantled in October 1947.

By contrast the four AA forts which had been erected in the Thames Estuary during the war survived, one of these was commandeered in the 1960s by pirate radio station Radio Caroline. Some of the Thames forts are still in existence.

In 1947 Henry Corkan was appointed Deputy Director of Bidston under Dr. Doodson. He continued research into the application of numerical methods to tidal problems, and in 1948 presented a paper 'Waves and Currents' to the Royal Astronomical Society.

In 1947 Dr. Doodson asked Mr. Jebson, Managing Director of A. Légé & Co., for an estimate of the costs of building a predictor of at least 35 components, together with an estimate for a machine with components on both front and back. In the latter case times and heights of tides could then be produced simultaneously, thus saving much time. Mr. Jebson's son, Maurice, produced an initial design which was acceptable and Dr. Doodson started work on designing the intricate workings of the machine. It would cost £4,150 to build a predictor to produce times and heights separately, (presumably a combined one would have been too costly at this stage), but the machine could be amended as finances permitted. The sale was dependent on the Tidal Institute being able to sell the old Kelvin machine to the French Hydrographic Service.

This was done in 1948, and the new 42 constituent machine, designed by Dr. Doodson and made by A. Légé and Company, was delivered to the Observatory in December 1950.

The Doodson - Légé tide-predicting machine

It was set up in the ground floor central room where the Kelvin had stood. By now the cost had risen to £5049, largely due to a National Wages Award of 4%. Légé's charge for sending a fitter to Birkenhead to assist in assembly was £376-12s-6d. Dr Doodson found this "incomprehensible." To quote him - "The fitter was here 8 days and we paid his complete hotel expenses and provided his lunch. I wish that I could be paid at the same rate!" The bill was settled by the University of Liverpool.

Sylvia Brooks (later Sylvia Asquith) joined the staff as a "computer" in February 1947 during a particularly severe winter. Coal was still rationed, and she recalls how each member of staff was requested to bring a piece of coal from home for the Observatory fire. As the junior girl she was delegated to take the mail to the Post Office each afternoon. The mail was first weighed and she was given the exact money to take with her, using the Observatory bicycle for transport. She trusted that the Post Office scales would agree with those at the Observatory!

She was required to make the coffee each morning. This was a bigger job than one might suppose. First she had to grind the coffee beans - just enough for that day's requirement. (Dr. Doodson insisted that the beans be freshly ground each morning). Sylvia then had to sprinkle the ground coffee onto a large pan containing a mixture half milk and half water placed on the gas heater (an added pinch of salt was mandatory). When the coffee was ready she had to pour it through a large sieve to remove the coffee grounds. The staff were served at their desks. Sylvia still recalls having to carry hot coffee down to the seismograph room in the lower cellars, the only light being provided by a dim red bulb.

There was only one car on site and that vehicle belonged to Dr. Doodson.

By 1st January 1948 salaries had reached the following levels (standard Mersey Docks and Harbour Board rates):-
J. R. Rossiter £425 per annum
Mrs. Joan Rossiter £220
Miss Margaret Harriman £200
Mrs. Sybil Hembrow £200
Miss Ainsworth £190
Alice Lewis £120
Joan Williams £120
Sylvia Brooks, Barbara Jones and Joyce Payne (all aged 17) £110
Margaret Cheeseman (aged 19) £120

Alice Lewis, Joan Williams and Margaret Cheeseman had all resigned before the end of the year. Many young recruits did not stay for long in those days. They found the work very laborious and often tedious. Working with numbers nearly all day, every day, proved too much for some of them. Those who took to the work tended to stay for many years. However marriage could bring the job to an end. Sybil Hembrow left her post on 11th August 1948. She had married one year earlier. Margaret Harriman, who married in June 1948 to become Mrs. Povall, was required to resign in July 1949 after nine years' service.

Herbert Bigelstone returned to Bidston in March 1948, but his love of meteorology led him to resign his position in December that year to take up a post in the West African

Service of the Colonial Office, where he would be providing B.O.A.C. (British Overseas Airways Corporation) with weather forecasts for their long-distance flights.

He is remembered as a tall, hearty character with a booming voice and a weakness for Garibaldi biscuits. He was essentially a meteorologist, less interested in tides. In his letter of resignation to Dr. Doodson he wrote, "At the close of nearly twenty years in close association, I would be grateful if you would accept - and convey to the Governing Committee on my behalf - my deep appreciation of the friendly and considerate treatment extended to me over so long a period. I shall always recall with pleasure the cordial spirit that has characterized our association and it is with some regret that I now ask that the association be broken."

In 1948 Dr. Doodson was appointed to the Hydraulics Research Board, and spent time working on a proposed barrage scheme for the River Severn. His research eventually led to the conclusion that the plan was impracticable and the scheme was abandoned.

A general assistant, Mr. H. Dempsey left on 24th April 1948. He was replaced by Mr. J. M. Morris at £4-11-6 per week. The latter apparently didn't like the job, for he left after one day, and was replaced by Joseph Balshaw. On June 20th 1949 Mr. Balshaw was replaced by Mr H. Dempsey - presumably the same gentleman returning to the post!

In March 1950 Dr. Doodson presented a paper entitled, "The levels in the North Sea associated with the storm disturbance of 8th January 1949", written by Henry Corkan, to the Royal Society. Later that year Henry Corkan was awarded a doctorate by the University of Liverpool.

(Courtesy Miss A. Corkan)
Members of staff pictured outside the front door of the Observatory early in 1950.
Front row:
Jack Rossiter, Dorothy Corkan, Henry Corkan, a visitor, Dr. Arthur Doodson, Mrs. Elsie Doodson, and Joan Rossiter.
Second row:
Joyce Sheldon, Barbara Jones, Sylvia Brooks, Eunice Heath, Bunty Marriott and Margaret Weston
Back row: Barbara Henshaw, Dorothy Ainsworth and Dorothy Render

Joan Rossiter resigned her post at Bidston in 1950, and the Rossiters subsequently had three children. At the time of her resignation Joan's salary had risen to £5 per week.

In the same year Dr. Doodson wrote to the Dock Board about the problems of retaining staff. His letter reads as follows: "March 11th - Dear Mr. Nelson,
At the next meeting of the Committee I shall have to report that I am having some difficulty in retaining the junior members of the staff. During the last year I have appointed three girls who have not stayed the full year. In two cases the plea for leaving was that the salary was not sufficient, but the girls

were not fully experienced in the work and had no special qualifications which would have justified them receiving a higher rate than other girls who are experienced in the work. I have not been able to do anything to retain their services. Similar difficulties arise in replacement.

We follow the Dock Board rates of pay, and the scale follows roughly the age of the girl. I have been reluctant to start new girls from other offices at the pay corresponding to age when they would be receiving the same rate as the girls of the same age who have been with me since leaving school and who are capable of doing the more difficult computations. It is important that I should do nothing to unsettle the experienced girls. Now the Dock Board rates are admittedly much lower than in many offices but there are certain compensations which have hitherto not applied to my staff. For instance, they get marriage allowances in the form of a gratuity of £15 after five years' service and £3 per year thereafter, and they also get superannuation benefits, and grants to dependents. Furthermore provision is made for a double increment of salary when a report is made as to the clerk having reached a certain proficiency in speed of shorthand or having attained a good standard of technical proficiency. We have not usually applied the last rule and I think that it would be only fair to the more experienced girls on the staff for the rule to apply. I would be prepared to recommend that three girls, now receiving the salary rate of £155 p/a be stepped up to the next rate of £170 p/a, and that any of the girls who become proficient in the special calculations required in the analysis of tides should in due course be able to look to receiving the special increment. After 12 years' service the senior girl, Mrs. Rossiter, is now leaving, and the new senior girl will be Miss Ainsworth, a very capable girl whose ability was recognised during the war by an enhanced salary. It has been our custom, however, when a girl reached this place of seniority to give her a special increase, as it is most helpful to have a responsible girl to care for the female staff. I would suggest that she also be stepped up to the next rate of pay, from £230 per annum to £245 per annum.

Owing to the unsettled conditions which exist at the moment we are tending to fall behind a little in the work and I wish to propose to the committee that we allow a measure of systematic overtime to be worked by the staff, with pay, as we had in force during certain periods in war-time.

I also wish to have permission to use the part-time services of past members of the staff, who may possibly be able to do some of the analytical and typing work at home, or possibly I might use the services this year of a local typing firm on the special work of typing the predictions for direct reproduction by the photolithographic processes used for the Admiralty Tide Tables. This will be an expense to us but not a loss as the Admiralty payment should cover the cost. I was in London last week and hoped that the Hydrographic Department would be able to assist in this typing work and so relieve the pressure on my most experienced girls, but I found that their difficulties were even greater than mine.

I am sorry to trouble you with so long a letter but the Committee would expect your views on the matter and I wished you to have all the details. If the work did not continue to increase we would be able to cope with the present situation without these abnormal measures.

Yours sincerely---"

Two new recruits to the staff at this time were Eunice Heath and Margaret Weston. Eunice had first met the Doodsons as a 13 year-old teenager. She remembers picnicking on Bidston Hill with a couple of friends when they were caught in a thunderstorm. They decided to knock on the door of the Observatory and ask for shelter. At this time the Doodsons employed a live-in housekeeper, Ena Mcloughlin, but it was the kindly Mrs. Doodson who invited them in to dry themselves in front of the fire, and gave them something to eat and drink, before they went on their way.

At this time predicting machines built by Légé & Co. for foreign governments, were inspected by Dr. Doodson before dispatch, and a Certificate of Efficiency was issued. There was a flurry of activity in this respect in the early 50s. Machines were built for the Philippines, Thailand, India and Argentina.

The machine built for the Siamese Government was exhibited in the "Dome of Discovery" at the South Bank Exhibition, London, during the Festival of Britain in 1951. This attracted much interest. Dr. Doodson wrote a short article entitled "Land and Sky, Air and Sea - a short sketch on the work of the Observatory" for the "Festival of Britain" brochure produced by the Birkenhead Council to mark the festival, and Bidston Observatory was opened to visitors in the afternoons and evenings. About 600 visitors, in parties of 20-25 were admitted. In his annual report Dr. Doodson acknowledged that "many more would have liked to come, but it was not possible to cope with more."

Many of the drawings produced at Bidston for the design of tidal prediction machines are still stored in the Bidston archive.

In April 1952 Dr. Doodson travelled to Monte Carlo to attend the Sixth International Hydrographic Conference for two weeks. His wife accompanied him, and they travelled by rail, boat and coach. Unfortunately both of them were unwell during the first few days of the trip, but Dr. Doodson described the visit as expensive but essential.

Dr. Doodson and Dr. Corkan prepared a joint paper, "Free tidal oscillations in a rotating square sea", intended for presentation to the Royal Society on November 13th 1952, but, tragically, Dr. Corkan was taken ill. He died unexpectedly of pneumonia, following on from pleurisy, in the Northern Hospital, Liverpool, before the presentation date, so Dr. Doodson presented the paper alone. Dr. Corkan was only 46 years old, and Dr. Doodson received numerous letters of condolence following his death, all remembering Dr. Corkan's great enthusiasm for his work, and the fact that he had had a promising career ahead as Dr. Doodson's intended successor. Dr. Corkan's wife, Dorothy, a former member of staff at Bidston, returned to work at the Observatory in order to provide for herself and their young daughter Audrey. Dorothy replaced a "computer" who had emigrated to India.

In a moving tribute to Dr Corkan, Professor Proudman said: "In the capacity of Deputy Director, Dr.Corkan did excellent work and was just beginning to receive world-wide recognition when he died in 1952. Through the untimely deaths of Grace and Corkan, Liverpool has been completely deprived of workers on tides of the generation next after Doodson's and mine."[1]

Fortunately another rising young scientist, John Rossiter, was waiting in the wings.

Dr. Doodson had been thinking about retirement as he approached the age of 60. However, rules dictated that his replacement be in possession of a doctorate. The loss of Dr Corkan meant that for the immediate future there was no suitably qualified member of staff available, so, for the time being, Dr Doodson was asked to remain in office.

Geoffrey Lennon

The gap left by Dr. Corkan was filled by Geoffrey Lennon, who took up the appointment in September 1952 at the age of 26. During the war Mr. Lennon had served with the Royal Artillery in Burma and Malaya.

Towards the end of that year, Dr. Doodson suffered an attack of angina, followed shortly afterwards by two attacks of coronary thrombosis. The death of Dr. Corkan had obviously added to the great strain on him. However, in 1953, he was offered a chance to recuperate on a seven week cruise in the Mediterranean, by the kindness of the Director of the Moss Hutchinson Line Ltd., which had commercial vessels in regular service there. Unfortunately

Dr. Doodson was not well enough to go in 1953, but eventually he and his wife were able to avail themselves of the offer in 1954.

In 1952 Professor Proudman received the C.B.E. and was awarded the Hughes medal of the Royal Society in 1957 for his work on dynamical oceanography, and in 1953 Dr. Doodson was made an Honorary Fellow of the Royal Society of Edinburgh. This was a great honour which had been awarded to only 22 British scientists over the years. In 1955 Dr. Doodson was awarded the C.B.E., an honour he had declined in earlier years when it had been offered in recognition of his war work.

At the end of January 1953 a disastrous storm surge in the North Sea caused severe flooding in SE England and in Holland where 1800 people lost their lives and damage was estimated at £200 million. A full investigation into the causes of the surge was carried out at Bidston and John Rossiter played a leading role. He lectured on the findings at The British Association in September 1953, and gave a talk on BBC radio as part of a series called "The Oceans" in June that year. In it he gave a very clear explanation of the cause of the surge. The content of the talk was printed in "The Listener" on July 8th 1954.

A meeting of the British Association was held at the University of Liverpool in September 1953. As part of the agenda, parties of 25 people visited Bidston on the 3rd and the 7th. Afternoon tea was provided at the Observatory, and transport was laid on by Crown Coachways of Manchester

St., Liverpool. Bidston produced tide tables for the locations on the itinerary - namely Freshfield, Southport, Hilbre Island, Parkgate, Frodsham and Menai Bridge, Anglesey.

In 1954 Professor Proudman retired from the Chair of Oceanography at the University of Liverpool. Two years later the University awarded him the Honorary Degree of LL.D. His wife Rubina died in 1958. Three years later he married for a second time. The bride was Beryl Waugh Gould, herself a widow.

In 1954 Dr. Doodson was closely involved in a further project to consider the possibility of setting up a barrage on the River Severn. A tidal model of the Severn Estuary was constructed, and for several months regular meetings were held with the Hydrographic Office and the Port of Bristol Authority. Eventually it was decided that the project was unfeasible.

Age discrimination was evidently not frowned upon in those days - In Dec 1954 a young man aged 24 applied to Bidston for a post, but was told the Mersey Docks and Harbour Board did not recruit clerical staff over 21 years of age!

By 1956 enough finance was available for components to be added to the back of the Doodson-Légé tide predicting machine, so that times and heights of tides could now be predicted simultaneously, thus cutting the time taken to produce a single prediction by more than a day. The machine was dismantled, and despatched to London by road in July 1956 for an expected absence of two months. By October the machine had still not returned. Dr. Doodson was concerned that the prediction work schedule was "getting completely upset." The machine was finally returned on Dec. 22nd, and Dr. Doodson and John Rossiter were kept busy (probably over the Christmas period) putting all in order.

John Rossiter obtained his M.Sc. in 1956 for a thesis entitled "The meteorological disturbance of water level." All his qualifications were achieved in his spare time by studying as an external student of the University of London.

Mr. Reynolds was a keen meteorologist on the Observatory staff from 1951 to 1957, with a particular interest in visibility (see Chapter Seventeen). He published several papers on the subject. He resigned from Bidston to take up a position with the North of Scotland Hydro Electricity Board as Inspector of Tide Gauges.

Correspondence shows that, in June 1956, Dr. Doodson required a handyman to work at the Observatory, preferably a retired man, so he contacted the Chief Constable of Birkenhead to see if a policeman, about to retire, would be interested in the post. None was available, so Dr. Doodson contacted the Chief Fire Officer with a similar query. A retired officer was found, but Dr. Doodson turned him down because of his asthma - he would not be able to attend to the heating furnaces. A man from Moreton was eventually taken on in August.

By now over 600 predictions were being supplied annually to Almanacs. Though many publishers preferred to publish time in the a.m. and p.m. system, and heights in feet and decimals, and to use special datums for certain docks, it was the policy of the Institute at that time to supply predictions only in 24 hour systems, with heights in feet and decimals based on Chart Datum (except in special circumstances) as otherwise there would be endless confusion. (All this was to change with the advent and versatility of computers).

Dr. Doodson's son, Thomas, became engaged to a member of staff, Valerie Boyes, but despite this she was still formally addressed as Miss Boyes during office hours. The young couple were married in the autumn of 1957, and for a time they lived in a caravan in the grounds of the Observatory.

Early in 1959 Dr. Doodson suffered from a cerebral thrombosis, followed by a third attack of coronary thrombosis. For a few months his ability to speak and write was affected. This may well have led to his decision to retire in 1960, at the age of 70.

At a party for 50 colleagues and friends, held at the Observatory, he was presented with an Atmos clock. In his retirement speech he referred to his "happy and prosperous relationship" with Professor Proudman, whom he described as a man of acknowledged genius. He regretted having to leave Bidston, saying that he felt it was "his baby."

Ex members of staff were invited to attend the retirement party, but many of them lived too far away to do so. However many of them sent good wishes to Dr. Doodson. Among them were Mrs A.Lesley Dennis, who had left Chester in 1949, and now lived, with her family, in London, working part time at a school; George Kirkland, who was now lecturing in mathematics and physics at a technical college in Kent; Sybil Henbrow, now in Bristol, and Barbara Truman Jones who had originally emigrated to Canada to work for the Tidal Survey but later moved to Africa where she met and married a university professor.

Mr. H.J.Bigelstone, in retirement after returning from Nigeria, was now running a post office in South Devon. In a tribute to Dr. Doodson he said, "I am sure I am only voicing the opinion of us all that we could not have had a kinder, wiser or more sympathetic guidance than that we all received from you."

Dr. Doodson took up residence in nearby Oxton with his wife.

Annual parties laid on by the Doodsons for the benefit of the staff had been a notable activity of the Doodson era - they were popular for "a good meal and games." A favourite game was the 'Paper Chase' - the staff searched for clues written on paper and hidden in the building or in the grounds. If it was after dark, the grounds had special lighting laid on for the purpose. 'Charades' was another favourite.

Dr. Doodson wrote to Légé & Co. to say that although he was now retired he would be happy to have his name still used in connection with tidal predictors.

John Rossiter was appointed Acting Director of the Liverpool Observatory and Tidal Institute.

Chapter Twelve

The Rossiter Years

Dr. John R. Rossiter

(Courtesy Proudman Oceanographic Laboratory)

The staff now numbered about fifteen, but turnover was still too rapid. Members of the junior staff were still called "computers." To quote the annual report of 1960 - "two computers have resigned and three have been added."

In June 1961 the Doodson-Légé machine was moved from the central room to a basement room in order to decrease fire risk. The charge for the work involved in dismantling and setting up was £360-7s-2d. Then in 1962 the time unit on the Doodson-Légé started slipping. A replacement one was borrowed from Légé & Co. in August and returned in October, as the old one seemed to have recovered. The following year the machine was damaged by an "inexperienced student" while he was setting up for a tidal prediction, and attempts by Institute staff to solve the problem failed. A mechanic was summoned from Légé & Co. to sort out the problem.

Over a long period of time Bidston and Légé & Co. had enjoyed a close relationship. John Rossiter was a frequent visitor to the factory in London, and on at least one occasion he dined with Mr. Maurice Jebson, the managing Director, at the Adelphi Hotel in Liverpool.

By the 1960s, however, the requirement for large tide predicting machines was giving way to prediction on the new electronic computers, particularly in Europe. Although Légé & Co. were now well established as a supplier of tide recorders for clients, they were still relying on foreign governments, such as those of Mexico, Burma and Indonesia, to maintain their tide predicting machine market. When Bidston revealed plans to sell its old Légé machine to Mexico, the Légé Company was unhappy about it, as for several years they had been negotiating to sell a new machine to Mexico.

Payment for some of the machines built for foreign governments was very slow in coming through to Légé & Co. and the end result was that they were able to pass over only a portion of the moneys due to Bidston. The relationship between the Tidal Institute and Légé & Co. came to an end.

In October 1960 the Mersey Docks and Harbour Board handed over complete control of the Observatory land and buildings, its instruments and appurtenances (free of expense) to the University of Liverpool. The Institute was renamed the University of Liverpool Tidal Institute and Observatory (TIO). John Rossiter, now Doctor Rossiter, was officially appointed Director by the Council of Liverpool University on 1st October, and the staff were assimilated into university grades and classed as technicians rather than as "computers."

Dr. Rossiter felt that electronic computing was the way of the future. In the TIO Annual Report for 1961 he said: "There can now be little doubt that the computer will prove of great value on tidal research in the future, particularly in the study of generation and propagation of tides and storm surges in seas and estuaries. But the relative merits of the computer and the orthodox analogue tide predicting machine in the routine tasks of tide prediction have still not been evaluated. What has been established, however, is that the prediction of hourly heights of tide can now be accomplished, as efficiently and, in some cases, more accurately by using the computer than by methods used before. In future all such routine predictions will be prepared on the computer."

A member of the TIO staff, Mike Murray, was assigned the task of writing a computer program designed to produce routine hourly height tidal predictions. He used the DEUCE computer at Liverpool University. This early computer was a huge, noisy machine comprising many cabinets, which almost filled a large room. Data input for Mike's program was on punched cards. These were laboriously prepared on small hand punches by junior staff at Bidston. The output was on paper tape. (I have vivid personal memories of the chaos which could ensue if the tape were accidentally dropped and unravelled). This tape was converted into typescript form using a Creed teleprinter.

Use of the Deuce computer had first been tried in October 1959, when the University undertook to perform a calculation on Dr. Rossiter's behalf. The calculation had been expected to take up two hours of computer time at a charge of £30 per hour. In the event the calculation took nearer six hours, but the University stood by the original arrangement and charged Bidston only £60.

Predictions were still being written up by hand, and, in those pre-photo-copier days, copies were still being made using the photographic equipment housed in a small basement laboratory at the Observatory. In 1961, the addition of a new 35 mm camera and enlarger made life a little easier.

All hourly height predictions and Harmonic Shallow Water Predictions (the latter being required for ports such as Southampton, which experience the multi-tidal patterns of the shallow Solent) were now being produced at Liverpool University on its new computer KDF9. This would hopefully prove more economical than the DEUCE. The formula for hourly tidal heights was fairly straightforward to translate into a computer program. Once the initial parameters had been set up, it was simply a case of advancing the time factor by one hour to produce the predicted tidal height for the following hour. High and low water predictions involved rather more complicated parameters, and more time was required to program these. Lever Brothers of Port Sunlight kindly made their computer facilities available to the Institute, as did the IBM Data Centre in London. As yet Bidston could not afford to purchase its own computer. Geoffrey Lennon, a senior scientist and lecturer at the Institute, and his assistant, Eunice Murrell (formerly Heath), did much commuting between Bidston and Lever Brothers in the early 1960s.

The old muzzle-loading cannon which had been sited on the observatory lawn since 1939 (see Chapter Fifteen) was donated to the City of Liverpool Museums in 1962, together with the Transit telescope and accessories (see Chapter Sixteen). These were intended for eventual display in the planned Maritime Museum.

A major appointment to the staff in 1962 was that of Norman Stuart Heaps, as researcher and lecturer.

Norman Stuart Heaps

(Courtesy Proudman Oceanographic Laboratory)

The ground floor living accommodation was adapted to house a resident caretaker-gardener, Mr. Seaton, who was appointed in 1962. He and his wife moved into the accommodation previously occupied by Dr. and Mrs. Doodson.

On a more personal note, I started work at Bidston Observatory on January 2nd 1962. It should have been January 1st, but I had received a phone call the previous day saying "Don't come in tomorrow - we're closed."

The scientists at the time were: - The Director (Dr. John Rossiter), Geoffrey Lennon, Norman Heaps and Mike Murray. The senior assistants were Mrs. Corkan - widow of Dr. Harry Corkan, Douglas (Doug) Leighton, Valerie Doodson - daughter-in-law of Dr. Doodson, and Eunice Murrell. A year or so later Glenna Stewart came in to join the science team. There were about seven junior lady assistants, of whom I was one. Our job was to observe the weather, to operate the tidal prediction machines, to fire the one-o'clock gun, to do 'differencing' - of which more anon - and to make the coffee for everyone and prepare lunch for the male staff.

The 'Met'
Bidston's weather records, amongst the longest in Britain, had been ongoing since 1866, during which time measurements of temperature, rainfall, windspeed and direction, and barometric pressure had been made every day of the year at 0900 GMT, and visibility and cloud amounts had been estimated by eye. The measurement of sunshine was added to the list in 1908. The seven of us worked a rota for Bank Holidays, including Christmas Day, and weekends. There

was no shortage of volunteers to work these extra duties, because, of course, it brought in an extra couple of hours' pay - time and a half for Saturdays, and double for Sundays and Bank Holidays. I recall that my starting pay was about £9 per week. Two of the more senior girls were in charge of the 'met'. This meant that they had the added responsibility of arranging duty rotas, and ensuring that all meteorological duties were covered, of producing weekly statistic reports for various clients, and writing up, by hand, a statistics sheet each month for the Met Office - Bidston was a climatological station reporting on a monthly basis to the Met Office. At the end of the month they also wrote up a summary of the month's weather for publication in the Liverpool Daily Post. This continued until the early 90s, when changing emphases at The Daily Post meant that past weather was no longer considered to be newsworthy. I well remember the 'ordeal' of dictating the report to the press newsroom over the phone. Sometimes this led to errors appearing in the press report, due to the typists in the newsroom being unfamiliar with the jargon. In later years we were able to fax the report through to the press.

Tidal Predictions
In 1962 we were using two tidal prediction machines, the Légé and the Doodson-Légé (D.L.). These were situated in two rooms in the basement of the Observatory. First we had to set up the machine for the seaport concerned. The machines each had 42 mechanical components. These represented the various contributions to the tide caused by the positions of sun and moon in relation to the earth, the shape of the coast around the port in question, etc. M2, the

component representing the twice daily pull of the moon on the sea surface, by far the largest factor in the tide, was correspondingly the largest mechanical component on the machine.

Amplitudes and angles had to be set on anything up to 42 components, amplitudes on the front of the machine and

angles on the back. The 42 components were connected by a system of wires and pulleys in such a way that all the constants (contributions to the time or height of a particular tide) were added together, and the result could be read off on the console. Preparing the machine for a port (such as Liverpool Princes Pier) could take up to two hours.

The M2 Component on the Doodson-Légé Tide Predicting Machine

Having 'set up' the machine we sat down at the console and operated the pedal. The predicted times and heights of the tides were read off and written down on large sheets of thick paper. We worked in two-hourly shifts at the console, and a full year of times and heights for any particular port would take about two days. The resulting figures were of course liable to human error, resulting from a misreading of the console or an incorrect writing-down. Although I recall that not too many errors crept in, the figures obviously had to be subjected to very thorough checking procedures. This brings me to 'differencing'.

Differencing

Most British ports experience two high tides and two low tides each day as the earth spins on its axis relative to the moon. The greatest variation between high and low water comes once a fortnight on the spring tides when sun, moon and earth approximately line up with each other, and sun and moon exert a combined pull on the sea. The least variation occurs two weeks later at neap tide when the sun and moon are approximately at right angles to each other as seen from earth. These variations can be plotted on graph paper, and should form smooth curves when a period of a month is plotted. On average tides advance between thirty minutes and one hour from one day to the next, e.g. 1000, 1035, 1115, 1200 and 1250 could be a sample progression over five days.

Differencing was the act of subtracting each day's tides, both times and heights, from those of the next day (mentally I might add - no calculators available in those days), and writing down the resulting figures. Thus we ended up with four columns of height differences and four columns of time differences for each month, written in pencil (pens not permitted). It took several hours to difference a port for the whole year, but it certainly kept our brains active.

The work was then passed to the 'smoother' - a more senior girl. She checked the figures by eye, underlining with a red pen anything that didn't look right, i.e. wouldn't produce a smooth curve if plotted. The work was then returned to the 'differencer' for her to check her figures. This uncovered the subtraction errors and those made in copying down from the predicting machine. The smoother would then correct any remaining errors by plotting the readings on graph paper and fitting a smooth curve to them. I would emphasise that there weren't too many of these problems, but the exercise was essential for accuracy.

Finally we came to the 'writing up' process. This involved neatly writing down all the figures on high quality A3 size sheets of paper, in ink, ready for the customer. Perhaps I should add that an ability to write figures neatly was an essential qualification for the job. The writing up had to be checked by close scrutiny in case any new errors had crept in. The sheets were then photographed in the Observatory 'dark room' before delivery to the client.

Three or four girls were involved in the process of developing and printing. They stood at large sinks containing developer, fixer, etc. and the negatives, all A3 size, were passed on from sink to sink until the process was complete. All this was done under a dim red light. I cannot recall ever having the privilege of being on the photography team. The photographic process was, at that time, the only way of keeping copies of the work for future reference, or if, God forbid, the pages should be lost in the post on the way to the client.

This whole laborious process meant that a year's predictions for a single port took about four days to complete, involving several people and about thirty man hours. By the 1990s every stage of the process (apart from packing) had been computerised. We merely typed into a computer the name of the port and the year required, and in a few seconds a smart laser printed copy of the figures was ready for the client. Provided the correct information had been fed into the computer, the predictions would be accurate and only a cursory check was required. The work of four days was reduced to about four minutes.

Sometimes Bidston was called on to produce information about the tides for some event in history. Requests for the state of the tide in the Wash when King John lost his treasure in October 1216 were a favourite, being sought from as far back as the 1930s. On another occasion we corrected the history books which claimed that William of Orange landed at Carrickfergus in the morning of June 14th 1690. Tidal calculations showed that he had to wait for high tide at noon.

Coffee and Lunch Duties

The junior assistants took it in turns to make coffee for the staff and prepare snacks at lunchtime. I recall that we had to boil up milk in a pan - the coffee must still be made half milk and half water. Coffee break started at 1045, on the dot, and finished at 1100 on the dot. The duty girl rang the bell in the round office. Three rings meant it was coffee time. All staff duly proceeded to the dining room, first door on the right off the entrance hall, where the girls sat at the tables and the men gathered round the beautiful marble fireplace. During the three years I was there in the early sixties, I cannot recall ever seeing a male member of staff sitting down at a table with the ladies - it simply was not the thing to do!

The lunchtime menu was rather limited as I recall - beans on toast, Ulster fry and tomatoes, or poached eggs.

About once a week, a baker's van drove up the hill, and we were allowed to go out and buy cakes - quite a luxury. A few years later the Stevenson Thermometer Screen on the lawn was flattened when the baker's van accidentally reversed into it. I suspect that may have ended the luxury of buying cakes on site!

There was still a well maintained vegetable garden, tended by Mr. Seaton, and I can remember occasionally being given runner beans or apples to take home.

I recall that in 1964 my announcement that I would be leaving to have a baby, caused great excitement at Bidston. It seems I had broken an imagined taboo, by being the first member of staff, for quite a number of years, to become pregnant. The other girls took great care of me. Repairs were being made to the driveway round the Observatory. This meant that, for a short time, staff had to cross rough ground to access the building. The girls were very keen to lend me a helping hand at such times.

Later in the year, after I had left, hovercraft trials were held between Leasowe and Rhyl. I am told that the staff rushed up on to the roof of the Observatory when they heard the roar of the engines (about two miles away) to watch the crossing.

In 1964 Mike Murray was awarded an M. Sc. by the University of Liverpool for his work on the analysis and prediction of tides using computers. Shortly afterwards he resigned from Bidston to pursue a career elsewhere. He was replaced by Graham Williams (the first of two staff members bearing that name!).

Meanwhile Dr. Rossiter worked for the Canadian government on a project investigating the effects of barrages on tides in the Bay of Fundy, which has the largest tidal range in the world.

On May 13th 1964 Bidston held an Open Day. There were about 100 invited guests, including Dr. Doodson and his wife, but the event was not designed for the general public. Staff had prepared 23 exhibits. These depicted current research topics, including "the investigation and forecasting of storm surges, the analytical treatment of mean sea level by a Permanent Service and the assistance given by the Institute in large scale civil engineering projects involving tidal problems, in addition to the well-known work of the Institute in providing tidal predictions for almost 200 major ports throughout the world."

In 1967, Dr. Doodson passed away. His funeral was attended by Bidston staff and University colleagues, past and present. His grave can be found in Flaybrick Cemetery in Birkenhead (Non-conformist section), less than a mile from the Observatory.

In a tribute to Dr Doodson, Professor Proudman said: "Having worked with Doodson for many years, I have been privileged to gain an intimate knowledge of his great qualities. These include the highest standards of honour, great personal kindliness and a keen sense of humour."[1]

Dr Doodson was much respected and loved by his staff who affectionately called him 'D', but never to his face of course. On the rare occasions when it snowed he had allowed them to toboggan on Bidston Hill, thus stretching the lunch hour somewhat.

His poor hearing was a problem throughout his life and he had designed his own hearing aid. It was a large, cumbersome affair by modern standards, and emitted a squeak of which its owner was not aware. He commented on the devotion to work shown by his girls whenever he walked into a room. They had their heads down because they had heard him coming! In 1961 he commented that he had tried "numerous hearing aids, valve sets and transistor sets, but the quality was not so good as the one I made myself, but their handiness compensates somewhat for that."

He was a firm disciplinarian, as a boy caught scrumping apples from the orchard found to his cost. The boy was locked in the dark observatory cellar for a time, before being allowed to go home.

The following extract from a letter sent to Mrs. Doodson by Rear Admiral G.S.Ritchie, Hydrographer of the Navy, at the time of her husband's death, gives some indication of Dr. Doodson's professionalism and expertise:

"Dr. Doodson had been very closely connected with the Hydrographic Department throughout his long service of 40 years at the Liverpool Tidal Institute, and this Department benefited very greatly indeed from his great wisdom. The science of Tidal Analysis and Prediction was very greatly advanced by his researches and workers in this field throughout the world have benefited enormously.

His collaboration with this Department was at all times very close. As you know he was part author of the Admiralty Manual of Tides, the standard treatise on the subject. We are also indebted to him for the Admiralty Methods of Analysis and Prediction, and in many other ways. Those, throughout the world, who work on this subject cannot fail to have been impressed by his great abilities and will feel the loss of his ever-helpful advice acutely.

I have no doubt that Dr. Doodson's work will always be referred to when any future tidal problems arise, and he has ensured for himself a most important permanent place in Hydrographic and Tidal history."

The amount of research done at Bidston increased considerably in the middle to late sixties. New researchers appointed to the staff included Dr David Pugh, Dr. Trevor Baker, Roger Flather, John Howarth, Tony Vanicek, Dr. A. J. Bowen and Sally Pinless. By 1967 the staff had increased to 34, and by 1969 it was 48.

Norman Heaps later spent six months in Wisconsin, USA, studying water levels on Lake Michigan. On his return, he introduced a series of fortnightly seminars to be held at Bidston, but open to outside visitors as well as staff, covering all aspects of science. These lectures particularly attracted students from the University, and the practice was still continuing into the 21st Century (the 'seminar' room on the first floor of the Proudman Building having been purpose-built).

In 1969 Dr. Rossiter was instrumental in arranging the transfer of Bidston from University control to NERC (Natural Environment Research Council). Professor Rosenhead, Professor of Applied Mathematics at the University, who had been a close associate and adviser to the Tidal Institute since its formation in 1929, conducted the negotiations on the University side. NERC was to assume financial responsibility for the Observatory, which was renamed ICOT (the Institute of Coastal Oceanography and Tides). Dr. Rossiter realized this would mean better pay and conditions for staff.

A press report issued at that time read:-
"A large-scale increase in equipment and activities at the Tidal Institute and Observatory on Bidston Hill was forecast last night by Dr. Rossiter the Director. Commenting on the news that the Government-sponsored NERC were to assume financial responsibility for the Institute, Dr. Rossiter said it meant that they would now be recognised as a National Institute dealing with problems in coastal oceanography and tides.

Dr. Rossiter said: 'We shall now be able to seek support for work that is required in coastal waters and have quite a reasonable chance of getting the necessary funds'.

A ship and a computer were two items which would now be within the Institute's reach.

'There will be an expansion of our staff and a broadening of our interests but this is going to take time. It will take a number of years to get things moving properly,' he added.

Prevention of the possible flooding of large areas of Central London under certain tidal and weather conditions is one of the problems currently being tackled at the Institute on behalf of the Greater London Council. Dr. Rossiter said he was particularly happy with the new arrangement because links with the University would be retained. 'In the past a lack of funds has restricted our work, but now we will be able to expand and continue our teaching and post-graduate school of studies,' he added."[2]

ICOT now became a component body of NERC, whose administrative headquarters were in Swindon, Wiltshire. NERC consisted of about 15 separate Institutes, scattered around Great Britain, each Institute specializing in its own field, e.g. British Antarctic Survey, British Geological Survey, National Institute of Oceanography, etc.

New research scientists were recruited to ICOT's staff. They included Dr. Ian Vassie, Dr. Joyce Banks and Mr. M. Amin.

ICOT and the Department of Oceanography at Liverpool University jointly celebrated their Golden Jubilee in 1969 with a dinner attended by past and present staff. Emeritus Professor Proudman, now 80 years of age, was the guest of honour. In his speech he recounted the history and development of both organisations.

To release more space in the Observatory the Doodson Légé tide predicting machine was sent temporarily to the Liverpool Museum, but because it was only on loan it was not officially put on public display. A new electronic computer, the IBM 1130 was installed in its place in the Observatory cellar. This modern computer, with its 16K store, card input and output, or alternative paper input, considerably enhanced the Institute's computing ability. Eunice Murrell and Mrs. Rankin operated the machine under Geoffrey Lennon's supervision.

The following year, a computer manager, Brian Robinson, and a systems analyst, Dr. Alan Davies, were appointed to be part of a team of six people responsible for computing at Bidston. At about the same time Dr. Leonard Skinner was appointed head of the new instrument section. It was Institute policy to buy instruments and equipment from commercial sources whenever appropriate, but there was a growing need for specialised, high precision instruments to be designed and built on site. Hence a drawing office and a mechanical workshop were required.

It was at this stage that Bidston's long history of recording weather statistics was nearly brought to an end. The rapidly expanding instrument section was urgently in need of a home, and there was no alternative but to house it in a prefabricated hut set up on the meteorological lawn on the north side of the Observatory. This meant that Bidston's meteorological site no longer conformed to the strict standards required by the Meteorological Office (M.O.) - the Stevenson screen and rain gauge were too close to the new instrument hut. As a result Bidston was dropped from the M.O.'s climatological network, and consideration was given to closing the meteorological department at Bidston altogether. However the needs of local authorities, together with the wishes of the local community and of the media, prevailed, and the meteorological observations continued.

Following on from research into the North Sea floods of 1953, a numerical model of the River Thames was set up in 1970. (To put it very simply - a numerical modeller breaks down an area being researched, such as the Irish Sea, into squares of equal area. Each square is represented by a mathematical formula. By varying the numbers in the formulae the researcher can test out the likely effect of strong wind, high tides, low atmospheric pressure, etc.). The scientists concerned were Dr. Bowen and Sally Pinless.

In December 1970 government approval was obtained for ICOT to start a detailed investigation into the feasibility of constructing a flood protection barrier for London at Silvertown, at a projected cost of £23 million. The idea was to test the effects, on a numerical model of the Thames, of closing a barrier at various stages of the tide.

The Thames Barrier

The project was a success, and construction of the Thames Barrier commenced in late 1974. It was operational by October 1982 and was used for the first time in February 1983.

An expansion of the Bidston premises was essential. During the next year Dr. Rossiter travelled regularly to Manchester to liaise with the architects designing a planned new building at Bidston. This building was to be named the Proudman Building in recognition of Professor Proudman.

By 1971 the amount of research work at Bidston was expanding rapidly and the staff now numbered 56. Norman Heaps, assisted by Eric Jones, a new recruit to the research staff, was developing a numerical tidal model of Morecambe Bay, as well as researching a three dimensional numerical sea model. Work was also being done by Stephen Loch on a computer model of the Mersey Estuary.

In 1971 members of staff at Bidston were involved in making a documentary about coastal flooding for Yorkshire Television. Filming took place both at the Observatory and on board the RRS John Murray. The use of NERC's research ships was now becoming available to ICOT, as had been foreseen by Dr. Rossiter. John Howarth made several short trips into Liverpool Bay on Vigilant in 1971-1972 to further his study of tidal currents, and Dr. Skinner led an 11 day trip into the Irish Sea on board RRS John Murray in October 1971 to test instruments designed and made at Bidston.

Alongside his many other commitments Dr. Rossiter was asked to present a paper on "The History of Tidal Predictions in the United Kingdom" to the Second International Congress on the History of Oceanography, due to meet in Edinburgh in September 1972. He began researching the topic in 1970, and the number of sources he tapped for that one paper is quite staggering. A large box, now at The World Museum Liverpool, is full of the research material he collected together. He became ill in May 1972 while still preparing the paper, and he did not live long enough to present it. It was with great sadness that we learnt of Dr. Rossiter's death from a heart attack. He died in Clatterbridge Hospital, Wirral, on May 16th at the early age of 52. His paper was read in Edinburgh by the Bidston librarian, Kathy Burke.

Geoffrey Lennon was appointed Acting Director, and one of his first duties was to acknowledge the many tributes to Dr. Rossiter which came in to Bidston from Canada, the U.S.A., Japan, Russia, India and many European countries. There are more than fifty such letters preserved in the Liverpool Museum Archives. We can only conjecture how much brilliant work was lost to science by Dr. Rossiter's premature death.

Obituary from the Daily Telegraph

"Dr. John Reginald Rossiter, whose study of tides and storm surges helped in planning London's £36 million flood barrier, to be built across the Thames at Silvertown, has died in hospital at Bebington, aged 52.
As Director of the Institute of Coastal Oceanography and Tides at Birkenhead, he investigated the new dangers to London. His conclusions became known as "Rossiterism."
They were based on the increase of tidal range which has been taking place over the last century resulting in rising high-water levels.
Dr. Rossiter, who gained his doctorate in science at London University, became known internationally as an expert on the effect of stormy weather on the sea surface." [3]

I had been very fortunate in having Dr. Rossiter as my boss during my early years at the Observatory, namely 1962-1964. He was a sincere and fair man, ever concerned for the welfare and needs of his staff. I recall how, in the weeks before I was due to leave to have my first baby, he had my desk moved from the first floor to the ground floor, to save me the effort of having to climb the stairs each day.

Dr. Rossiter's brother, Leonard, became well-known in a very different sphere, that of television and the stage.

Over the years, Professor Proudman, Dr. Doodson, Dr. Corkan and Dr. Rossiter had all made huge contributions to the advancement of scientific knowledge throughout the world.

Chapter Thirteen

The Bidston Story Continues

The new Proudman Building was due to be completed by mid-1975. In the meantime extra space was desperately needed, so a suite of recently-built first floor office premises situated close to the centre of nearby Moreton was acquired. In February 1973 three Bidston departments - Computational, Systems Analysis and Permanent Service for Mean Sea Level (PSMSL) (See Chapter Twenty-one) moved out to Moreton for a few months - a total of 25 staff were involved.

I thought about returning to work when my younger son was seven years old, and was fortunate to be offered work in the Earth Tides Section (See Chapter Twenty-one) at Bidston on a casual basis. Shortly afterwards I obtained a permanent part time post in the Computational Section, doing tidal predictions, and, as it was late 1972, I soon found myself stationed in Moreton. Working in a town centre proved a noisy contrast to life on Bidston Hill, but it was very handy for shopping! Even in Moreton we were short of space. I can recall an afternoon part-timer coming in at 1 p.m. and telling me it was time I went home as she needed the desk for the afternoon! Most of the girls responsible for the Meteorological observations were stationed in the Computational Section at Moreton, so roughly one week in six was spent back at Bidston monitoring the weather, and of course we still had the weekend Meteorological rota to operate up at the Observatory.

Demand for research ships to carry out the deployment and testing at sea of instruments, such as current meters and tide gauges, was increasing by 1972. R.R.S. John Murray was extensively used in the Irish Sea, and high demand from other NERC Institutes to use the ships meant that Bidston had to rely on chartered vessels quite often. The Lady Francis, a 24 foot auxiliary sloop, and the Lass O'Dee, a 30 foot Scottish lobster boat, were both hired in the spring and summer of 1972 for research work in Liverpool Bay.

On June 1st 1973, the Institute of Oceanographic Sciences (IOS) was formed by the merging of I.C.O.T., the National Institute of Oceanography (NIO), the Unit of Coastal Sedimentation, and the part of the NERC Research Vessel Base which was concerned with scientific equipment for use at sea. NIO was located in Wormley, Surrey, the Unit of Coastal Sedimentation was based in Taunton, Devon, and the home base for the Research Vessels was sited in Barry, South Wales. The staff of NIO were specialists in the physics and chemistry of the open ocean, while, of course, those at ICOT were experts on tides and related phenomena. This new Institute comprised about 350 staff, and its Director was Professor Henry Charnock, former Professor of Oceanography at Southampton University. He was stationed at Wormley, and Dr. David Cartwright was appointed Assistant Director

(IOS) in charge of Bidston. He moved house from Wormley to Heswall. Mr. Michael Tucker was appointed Assistant Director (IOS) in charge of Taunton and of the IOS group at Barry, and his previous position as Head of Applied Physics at NIO Wormley was taken up by Dr. Brian McCartney.

In June 1974 Mr. Lennon visited the Department of Transport in Melbourne, Australia, in connection with a tidal survey of the Torres Strait. The country must have made a good impression on him, and he on it, as future events were to show.

A poem, written at about that time by an unidentified staff member, describes the duties of the junior staff at Bidston quite well. It reads:-

My name is ......,
I do the M.S.L.,
Port Patrick, Belfast, Dover,
Are ports I know quite well.
From hourly heights on tidal graphs,
Related to gauge zero,
I list the months' and yearly means
of levels of the sea. Oh....
of course you must be wondering
just how I manage this.
There is a vital program
That is written on a disc,
To help me sort the numbers out.
I hope you understand
Although I will admit to you

It was once done by hand.
The computer spares me time for
some other vital tasks.
Punching and checking data,
Met. obs. and lots of graphs.
I operate the switchboard too,
Can even make the coffee,
John ......'s current data work,
How could you not upgrade me?

Quite a number of romances blossomed at Bidston over the years:-
In 1934 Dorothy Dodd had married Henry Corkan, and in 1945 Joan Duckworth married John Rossiter, the future Director. In 1957 Valerie Boyes married the Director's son, Thomas Doodson, and, a few years later, Margaret Weston married Geoffrey Lennon. In future years Sue Ashton would marry John Howarth, Jane Foster would marry Graham Jeffreys, Carol Jones would marry Dr. David Pugh, Elaine Barrow would marry Bob Spencer, Sheila Brown would marry Tony Shaw, Jean Philpotts would marry Robert Smith, and Julia Hargreaves would marry James Annan. (Apologies to any I have missed off the list!)

Research at sea was now making a vital contribution to IOS science. During 1975 about 80 cruises were made by vessels either belonging to NERC or chartered by the Council. A fire broke out in the engine room of RRS Discovery just before midnight on 2nd November 1975, while she was cruising near the Azores. A member of the engine room watch, Mr. W. R. Jones, was killed, and RRS Discovery was out of commission for several months. NERC's other vessels at that time were RRS John Murray, RRS Shackleton and RRS Challenger.

In his annual report for 1975 Professor Charnock emphasised the progress of the Tides Group, now almost entirely located at Bidston. Tidal data was increasingly needed for analysis and research purposes, so that improved tidal predictions could be produced. This data was obtained from the Tide Gauge Network (See Chapter Twenty-one).

By now the Tidal Computation Section, using modern computer programs, was annually producing about 140 standard port tide predictions for hydrographic departments and port authorities world wide, and 185 secondary port predictions for other sites around the coast of Great Britain. The latter predictions were generally required by seaside resorts, publishers of almanacs and diaries, or by the press. A Linatron machine, using computer assisted typesetting, had recently been installed at Bidston, and could produce fully formatted tide tables ready for publication - no more laborious writing up by hand!

Space in the Observatory was still at a premium, as the new Proudman building was not yet completed. The library was moved downstairs to occupy what had previously been the dining room. The staff were temporarily relegated to eating lunch in the small kitchen or at their desks. The lovely marble fireplace which had graced the dining room was sadly broken up, but I am told that a few people managed to rescue some chunks and have them made into ashtrays. On the plus side reading facilities for the scientists were greatly improved.

A Honeywell 66/20 computer was due to be installed at Bidston in early autumn 1976, but the associated air conditioning plant was delayed, and resulted in a cutback for some of the planned projects. In the meantime IOS was able to use the computing facilities at the Science Research Council's laboratories at Daresbury and Rutherford. An in-house computer network was set up in 1976. This meant that timesharing terminals were now available in laboratories and offices.

In March 1977 Geoffrey Lennon and his wife Margaret (née Weston), a former staff member at Bidston, moved to Adelaide, South Australia, where Mr. Lennon had been offered the Chair of Oceanography at Flinders University. For the next 17 years Professor Lennon fulfilled many important roles. Despite the distance involved he continued to fill the role of Director of PSMSL although the work was based at Bidston. He was largely responsible for the setting up of the Australian Tidal Prediction Service. A tidal station on Macquarie Island was named the Geoff Lennon Sea Level Station in his honour.

On the Queen's Birthday, in June 1994, Professor Lennon was awarded the A.O. (Officer in the Order of Australia). In the British Imperial Honours List this award lies between Knight Bachelor and Order of the Bath.
Following his retirement Professor Lennon was appointed Emeritus Professor, and became a Fellow of the Royal Society of South Australia.[1]

During the winter of 1977-78 a data link was set up between the Meteorological Office's Central Forecasting Office in Bracknell and Bidston, so that real-time sea level forecasting tests could be introduced at Bidston.

Extensive new instrument laboratories were now available in the basement of the new Proudman Building, so that the workshop shed set up on the lawn of the Observatory in 1970 was no longer needed and could be taken down. As a result the Bidston Meteorological station once again complied with Meteorological Office requirements and was duly re-instated as an official climatological station.

The Honeywell 66/20 computer was further delayed, and recourse was made in the meantime to other NERC computers and to the Honeywell's Acton Data Centre. The 66/20 eventually became fully operational at Bidston in January 1978. It consisted of a number of large cabinets, some taller than a person and almost completely filling the purpose-built suite which occupied a large portion of the ground floor of the new Proudman Building. I recall how the heat and volume of noise from the computer were almost overpowering as one entered the room. The operators evidently got used to this!

At this time research work was greatly assisted by use of the powerful Cray-1 computer of the SRC (Science Research Council) at Daresbury in Cheshire. One of the Bidston scientists, Dr. Joyce Tranter (née Banks), conveniently lived in Daresbury. I can recall her often arriving at Bidston in a morning, loaded with computer output which she had collected en route to work.

In 1978 Martyn Lees, aged 28, a scientist at IOS Taunton, was tragically lost overboard while working on a chartered vessel at anchor in the Bristol Channel. This was the first and, thankfully, only death of an oceanographer of the Institute while working at sea.

Towards the end of 1978 the Government announced an increase in funds allocated to NERC. Plans were made for new research activities in IOS, but the change of government in May 1979 brought cuts in public spending, and most of the hoped-for funds were not forthcoming. In fact NERC had to impose a 4% staff reduction, and IOS lost 12 posts, mainly by natural wastage. The planned cruise program for 1981/82 was cut back.

The official opening ceremony for the Proudman Building was held on the 18th April 1979, and the building was named

The Proudman Building

This photo, taken about 1980, gives an indication of staff numbers at that time. (Courtesy John McLeod Photos)

by the Chairman of NERC, Professor Sir James Bearment, FRS. It is a pity that Professor Proudman, who had died in a nursing home in Fordingbridge, Hampshire, on 28th June 1975 at the age of 87, did not live to see the building which had been named after him. However his widow Beryl and one of his sons were able to attend the ceremony.

In 1985 there was considerable disquiet when NERC decided to slim down IOS for economic reasons. This meant that either the Bidston or the Taunton site would be closed down. To the relief of staff at Bidston it was decided to close the Taunton site, and to concentrate work at Wormley and Bidston. Many of the 49 staff at Taunton resigned or took early retirement, and only five moved to Wormley. Six relocated to Bidston to continue their sedimentation research here. They included Dr. Keith Dyer, who was temporarily put in charge of the Bidston Laboratory, following on from Dr. Cartwright's decision to return to Wormley to spend a year (before retirement) back on home ground.

Efforts by the former Taunton scientists to rebuild the Sedimentation Group at Bidston unfortunately failed, partly due to lack of resources and partly due to lack of suitable applicants. As a result most projects had to be abandoned.

The research ships, RRS Discovery and RRS Challenger were laid up for most of 1985 due to the financial squeeze.

Tom Dugdale, who had served on the Administration staff for many years, retired in 1985 and was awarded the MBE for services to Bidston. The year also marked the retirement of Mick Connell, who had long been general handyman at the Observatory and had lived, with his family, in one of the lighthouse cottages since 1937.

Tragically, Dr. Norman Heaps died on 26th June 1986 from lung cancer at the early age of 51 following a brilliant 24 year career at Bidston. Ironically, he had never smoked. He was a great loss to the scientific community, having done much research work, published many papers and travelled widely. In a tribute to him, Dr. Laughton, Director of IOS, said "He gave a lifetime of distinguished and valuable service to the Institute at Bidston, developing computer models for tides and storm surges for the seas around NW Europe and leading a program of physical oceanography."

I remember him as a quiet, gentle man, who never raised his voice in anger. He was a devout Methodist, and a great love of his life was fell-walking. On one of his last walks over the Cumbrian Fells, he said to his companion, "You know, I've achieved most of the work I set out to do 25 years ago and I count myself lucky to have had the opportunity to do so."
In December 1986 Dr. Dyer resigned as Acting Officer in charge of Bidston in order to return to his Devon roots to become Director of the Plymouth Polytechnic Institute of Marine Sciences, and to set up a new program in sedimentation. Dr. John Huthnance was temporarily put in charge of IOS Bidston.
In January 1987, after a distinguished career in the study of tides and sea level, Dr. Cartwright retired from IOS, and went to work for the Goddard Space Center of NASA in the USA.

Soon after this, NERC decided to separate IOS managerially into two separate Institutes which would be autonomous within the Marine Sciences Directorate of NERC. From April 1st 1987 Bidston would be known as the Proudman Oceanographic

(Courtesy Colin Bell)

Laboratory, named after Professor Proudman, and Wormley would be the IOS Deacon Laboratory, named after Sir George Deacon, founder and first Director of IOS.

Dr. Brian McCartney
(Courtesy Proudman Oceanographic Laboratory)

Dr. Brian McCartney, who had been head of the Applied Physics Group at Wormley for 14 years, was appointed Director at Bidston.

Sir Peter Harrop, Chairman of the UK Committee for the European Year of the Environment, carried out the formal renaming ceremony at Bidston during an Open Day on June 9th. This was attended by over 100 official guests, including senior representatives of NERC, the Hydrographer of the Navy, and guests from government, academia, industry and commerce. On this occasion both of Professor Proudman's sons, Colonel J. Proudman and Professor I. Proudman were able to be present. The following day over 1000 members of the public toured the buildings. The Open Days proved so popular that they were repeated the following year, June 1988. This time the number of visitors reached 1300, and included local MPs who had not been available the previous year due to election commitments.

The work of the Laboratory was now largely research based, and came under four headings:-

1. CRP1 (Community Research Project 1) - The North Sea Project.
Bidston acted as 'host' laboratory to this Project, which involved three NERC Marine Laboratories and ten University or Polytechnic Departments, studying the balance between exploitation and conservation of the North Sea. RRS Challenger was used continuously for a fifteen lunar month period, starting in August 1988, to collect deep sea data from various locations in the North Sea. John Howarth of Bidston co-ordinated the Project, and scientists from several other NERC Institutes were involved. The successful completion of the Project was marked by a party held on Board RRS Challenger in October 1989.

2. LRP1 (Laboratory Research Project 1) - Dynamics of Shelf and Sea Slopes.
This was concerned with understanding the natural environment of the seas on the comparatively shallow Continental Shelf around the UK coast.

3. LRP2 - Sea levels, Ocean Topography and Tides.
The PSMSL continued its work of extracting sea level data

from observations with the object of building up a picture of sea level changes worldwide, as a contribution to the study of climate change.

4. LRP3 - Technology Development.

This involved all aspects of the design and production of

scientific equipment for the use of the above projects.

Myrtle was designed and constructed in the Bidston workshop. It was successfully used from 1992 to 1996 to measure deep ocean sea level over a period of five years from a depth of 2.4 kilometres in the Antarctic Ocean. (A new improved version was deployed in the year 2000).

The above photgraph shows MYRTLE (Multi Year Return Tidal Equipment). (Courtesy Proudman Oceanographic Laboratory)

In February 1990 severe storms, caused by a combination of gale force WNWly winds, high spring tides and low atmospheric pressure caused a build-up of water on the coasts of North Wales and Merseyside (see photo).

The photo shows the flooded promenade at New Brighton on 19/20 February 1990

The flooded area at the landward side of the bathing pool

Severe flooding was experienced at Towyn on the North Wales Coast and at New Brighton on the Wirral. This led to particular investigation by the staff of LRP2. The bathing pool at New Brighton was so badly damaged that it had to be demolished within a few days. (see photo)

As computer development advanced, so the size of computers decreased. The new IBM 4381 mainframe computer required considerably less space than its Honeywell predecessor, and could be housed in a smaller room. The old Honeywell computer room was converted into a library, and the old library in the Observatory duly became an office for the use of the Tidal Computations Section. A Local Area Computer Network was set up at Bidston. This meant that many members of staff now had access to personal computers which were connected to the central IBM 4381 mainframe. Staff now had access to much more information at the mere touch of a button.

The Gulf War of 1990 brought an interesting project to the staff of LRP3. In one month they produced an operational model to simulate the oil leak from the Al Ahmadi terminal. This involved bathymetry values provided by BODC, tidal predictions for Gulf Ports produced by the Tidal Computation

Section, and a modified tides plus surge-currents and dispersion model, together with a module simulating the physical chemistry of oil provided by Dr. A. J. Elliott of UCNW (University College of North Wales). The resulting information was used by the Department of the Environment to advise personnel dealing with the spill at Al Ahmadi.

Occasionally female members of staff had the opportunity to join research cruises. In late October 1991 I was invited to join RRS Challenger at quite short notice, as a weather observer. We were at sea for nearly three weeks cruising round the Shetland Islands, retrieving current meters and taking CTDs (current, temperature and density readings). The weather was particularly bad. We experienced frequent hail and snow, and on ten of the days the wind reached force 8 -10. The captain remarked that the swell was the biggest he had met in a lifetime at sea. Surprisingly enough I was not at all seasick, although many of the younger

RRS Challenger

scientists did succumb. I was told that this was because the ears of older people are less sensitive to the movements of the ship! However, making meteorological observations from the bridge every hour from 0800 to 2300, meant climbing a steep gangway in all weather, and I arrived home with legs looking extremely black and blue!

A reward came on the evening of November 8th, for once a calm night, when we observed a spectacular auroral display. Red, white and grey beams, like searchlights, covered most of the sky. The complete blackness which surrounded us - not a shore light or another ship on the horizon in any direction - only served to emphasize the effect.

In 1992 Bidston's weather station finally succumbed to the inevitable and became automatic. It was no longer considered viable to have staff attending every day of the year to observe the weather, particularly as the national trend was now towards long holidays at Christmas and New Year. For a while the two methods of observation ran in tandem, until we were fully satisfied with the automatic readings. A method of converting radiation readings from an automatic recorder into hours of sunshine was successfully reached. This followed long term comparisons with the tried-and-tested method, in use since 1908, of recording burns made by the sun's rays shining through the solid glass sphere of a Campbell Stokes sunshine recorder onto specially treated cards.

Unfortunately observations of cloud and visibility fell victim to the new system, as at that time there were no instruments available which would have satisfied our requirement. It would have been difficult to continue observing visibility in any case, as the view from the Observatory roof was now being obscured by the tall trees. These were protected by law and could not be pruned. The hill was becoming a very different place from the open heath land of 1909 (see pictures below).

This card postmarked 1909 shows how the hill was mainly heath-covered at that time.

In 1992 POL's involvement in CRP1 (North Sea Project) came to an end, and was replaced by a new Community Research Project called LOIS (Land-Ocean Interaction Study). This would involve research along the coastal zone and on the Continental Shelf edge, namely the areas bordering the North Sea Project zone. The project leader for the coastal zone project (Coastal and Shelf Interactions) was Dr. Roger Flather, and the Continental Shelf edge leader (Ocean-Shelf Interactions) was Dr. John Huthnance (Marine Sciences Directorate).

In this photograph, taken in February 2005, the Observatory is barely visible. The exact 1909 viewpoint is inaccessible and from it the Observatory would not be seen at all.

The ongoing design of ever more powerful computers meant that yet another computer system was installed at Bidston. The IBM 4381 was de-commissioned in June 1993, and a

UNIX system replaced it. Each time the computer system was changed, all software programs, e.g. for tidal prediction, needed modifying. Fortunately we had a very helpful NCS (NERC Computing Services) Local Support team, headed by Dr. Colin Stephens, to take the strain. In 1994 the UNIX system consisted of a server and 58 individual workstations.

In 1994, following the publication of a government white paper called 'Realizing our Potential', POL lost its independence and became part of CCMS (Centre for Coastal and Marine Sciences). Once again three Institutes were involved. POL was grouped with the Plymouth Marine Laboratory (PML) and the Dunstaffnage Marine Laboratory (DML) in Scotland. Dr. Brian Bayne from PML was appointed Director of CCMS.

The photograph shows members of Bidston staff - Joyce Scoffield, Colin Bell and Helen Jones - meeting Prince Edward, watched by members of The Ocean Youth Club. The Prince's Equerry is studying the POLTIPS package.

Meanwhile, life at Bidston was not without its high points. In 1994 three members of the Tidal Prediction Section had the honour of travelling to the London Boat Show at Earl's Court to present a tidal prediction program POLTIPS (on disk) to the Patron of the Ocean Youth Club. For security reasons the identity of the Patron was not revealed to us till arrangements had been made. The Patron turned out to be Prince Edward. He asked us numerous questions about Bidston. It was a nerve-racking, but very enjoyable and memorable occasion.

Valerie Doodson retired in 1996 after 40 years continuous employment at Bidston. She was awarded the M.B.E. for her services to P.O.L. and to charity.

This photo was taken in 1996 when the domes were in the process of renovation.

In 1997 Dr. Bayne resigned in order to take up an appointment in Australia, and Dr. McCartney was Acting Director of CCMS for a few months. Professor Jacquie McGlade succeeded Dr. Bayne as Director of CCMS.

Dr. McCartney reached retirement age in May 1998 following a distinguished career. He was succeeded as Director of CCMS Bidston by Dr. Edward (Ed) Hill.

In the year 2000 N.E.R.C. decided to disband CCMS, and POL once more became an independent Institute under NERC administration. Several compulsory redundancies followed.

In September 2000, staff at POL produced a numerical model of Sydney Harbour which was used, together with local wind information, to forecast tidal current movements in the Harbour during the ten day period of the sailing competition in the Olympic Games. This was of great assistance to the British Sailing Team who won three gold medals and two silver medals.

In July 2003 POL's expertise on ocean currents was put to good use when Dr. Roger Proctor took part in the Channel 4 TV program "Battlefield Detectives", which attempted to explain the fate of the Spanish Armada.

The imminent closure of the site meant that Bidston's long-standing weather station, dating from 1867, could no longer be maintained, and this was closed down in November 2004.

However real-time weather conditions on Hilbre Island can now be accessed via POL's website (www.pol.ac.uk). The information is updated every ten minutes. A webcam is also sited on Hilbre. This gives panoramic views, updated hourly, of the area around the island. The two facilities form part of the new Coastal Observatory set up by POL staff to monitor the coastal sea's response both to natural forces such as the weather and to the consequences of human activity.

In December 2004 POL moved to new purpose-built premises at the University of Liverpool, whilst remaining under NERC administration, thus ensuring close contact between NERC and the University. In spring 2005 Dr Ed Hill moved to Southampton to take over as Director of NOCS (National Oceanographic Centre, Southampton), which is owned jointly by the University of Southampton and NERC. The new Director of POL is Professor Andrew Willmott. He was formerly Professor of Applied Mathematics and Head of the School of Computing and Mathematics at the University of Keele, as well as being Director of the Keele Centre for Wave Dynamics.

Professor Willmott's aim to take POL's program of research forward and to encourage more collaboration with partner institutes is already being realised. The Liverpool Bay Coastal Observatory is to be the centre of an international network for Coastal Observing Systems, and the National Centre for Ocean Forecasting (NCOF), which opened in Exeter in March 2005, involves collaboration between the Met Office, Plymouth Marine Laboratory, POL, NOCS and the Environmental System Science Centre in Reading. It aims to provide an ocean forecasting service similar to the Met Office's weather service, by providing 5 to 10 day forecasts of surface waves, storm surges, sea ice, ocean temperatures, salinities and currents for the deep ocean and for shelf and coastal seas. The data will provide support for, among other things, oil slick response, search and rescue, wind farms, response to coastal flooding and the safety of shipping.

POL is part of the UK Consortium membership of the Partnership for Observation of the Global Ocean (POGO) which is intended to build links world-wide among oceanographic institutions to promote long-term co-operation in comprehensive global-ocean observations.

The Permanent Service for Mean Sea Level (PSMSL), the British Oceanographic Data Centre (BODC) and the National Tide and Sea Level Facility (See Chapter Twenty-one) now operate from the Liverpool site, together with the Applications Group, the Ocean Engineering and Technology Group (building and using new and innovative instruments), and the many other groups involved in oceanographic research.

POL continues to be a world centre for tidal prediction and is a leading European centre for the modelling and forecasting of shelf sea dynamics. The Applications Group supplies tidal predictions, a software package to predict coastal tides and another to predict off-shore tidal elevations and currents. The Group produces numerical models of the seas around the British Isles, as well as for areas further afield, which can be used to indicate tide-surge levels. It also produces educational software for schools. It operates a consultancy service for industry, academia and the general public, acting as a bridge between POL research and the outside world.

This, then, has been the story of an unremarkable hill-top which, initially at the behest of and for the benefit of the Liverpool shipping interest, has served generations of seafarers and the wider community. From the ingenuity of the flag and the semaphore systems, through the application of science to problems of position and time, to scientific research into tides and oceanography, the story has been one of solving pressing problems with practical solutions. It is, therefore, the history of the people who have worked on this hill-top, contributing remarkably to the sum of human welfare and progress in their chosen fields.

Now, Bidston's connection with Liverpool and the sea is apparently finished. At the time of writing, the future of the Bidston Observatory complex is obscure, but the Bidston Preservation Trust would like to turn it into a museum. It is to be profoundly hoped that a place with such a magnificent history will be able to retain the glory of its past.

Chapter Fourteen

Four Directors: Their Early Years

John Hartnup

John Chapman Hartnup was born at Hurst Green in Sussex on 7th January 1806. He displayed an enthusiasm for astronomy, and took up a post as assistant at John Wrottesley's private observatory at Blackheath on the outskirts of Greenwich Park. While there John Hartnup made valuable contributions to the Wrottesley Star Catalogue.[1]

John Wrottesley, eight years senior to John Hartnup, was a founder member of the Royal Astronomical Society (RAS). He did an enormous amount of observational work, for which he was awarded the RAS Gold Medal. In 1841, on the death of Lord Wrottesley, his son, John, succeeded to the title, and moved to the family estate near Wolverhampton. There he built a new observatory. He was President of the Royal Society from 1854 -1858. He died in 1867, and it seems his enthusiasm for astronomy was not shared by his descendants, as, apparently, very little of his observatory now remains.

Meanwhile, John Hartnup had moved on to be a "supernumary" at the Royal Greenwich Observatory, later becoming Assistant

Secretary to the RAS. He married Elizabeth, five years his senior, in Kent in the spring of 1839. At some stage they moved into one of the RAS apartments at Somerset House. Their son, also called John, was born there in 1841.

John Hartnup resigned his position at the RAS in order to take up the post of Astronomer to Liverpool, and moved into the newly built Waterloo Dock Observatory with his wife and three-year-old son in 1844.

William Edward Plummer

William Edward Plummer was born in Deptford on 26th March 1849. He was the younger son of John and Sarah Plummer, their elder son John Isaac having been born there in 1845. William was educated privately.[2]

The nearby observatory at Greenwich probably attracted both boys to a career in astronomy. John Isaac became an assistant astronomer, first at Glasgow Observatory, then at Durham, before moving to Colonel George Tomline's private observatory at Orwell Park, Ipswich. When this closed he joined the Colonial Observatory in Hong Kong as an assistant.

Meanwhile, at the age of fifteen, William Plummer joined the astronomy department at Greenwich as a "supernumerary computer" - just as John Hartnup had done about forty years earlier. William was soon allowed to make occasional observations using the Transit-circle telescope. After three years, in 1868, he moved to Twickenham to work at the private observatory of Mr. George Bishop Junior, whose father had established an observatory in Regent's Park. William learned much from John Russell Hind, who had overall supervision of the observatory, and who, at the same time, filled the post of Superintendent of the Nautical Almanac Office. William's duties, during that period, were to observe comets, to compute their orbits and to complete zodiacal charts. He calculated the return of Brorsen's Comet, named after the Danish astronomer Theodor Brorsen who first discovered it in February 1846, to within half a day, and William Plummer claimed that he was the only Englishman, apart from Halley, to predict the return of a comet. He was elected a Fellow of the Royal Astronomical Society on 9th May 1870.[3]

While at Twickenham, the 23 year old William married Sarah, a year his junior, in autumn 1871 and a daughter, Alice, was born there in 1872.

When the Oxford University Observatory was set up in 1873, under the directorship of Professor Pritchard, Plummer was asked to be First Assistant. He held this post for the next nineteen years. Professor Pritchard was elderly and suffered from ill health. As a result much responsibility fell on Plummer's shoulders. For instance he represented the professor at a meeting in Paris in 1891, and was largely responsible, with a colleague, Jenkins, for the contents of four published volumes of astronomical observations, including photographic astronomy used for the first time.

A son, Henry Crozier, was born to the Plummers in Oxford in October 1875. Henry shared his father's interest in astronomy and also worked for a short time at the Oxford University Observatory. He was elected to the Royal Astronomical Society in 1899. A second son, Paul, was born in Oxford in 1884.

I have found no details of formal qualifications held by William Plummer. However, he was awarded an honorary degree of M.A. by Oxford University in 1889, when he was 40 years old.

He was elected a Fellow of the Royal Astronomical Society in May 1879 and served on the committee 1889 -1894. His second love, after astronomy, was playing chess.

Joseph Proudman

Joseph Proudman was born on 30 December 1888 at Thurston Fold Farm, Unsworth, near Bury, where his father, John Proudman, was a farm bailiff. Joseph attended primary school at Unsworth from 1894 until the family moved to occupy a tenant farm at Bold, near Widnes, in 1898, where he became a pupil at Bold Heath Primary School until 1902.

For the next five years he was a pupil-teacher at Farnworth Primary School, between Bold and Widnes. His salary, £6 10s. 0d. per year in 1902, had almost quadrupled to £24 per year by 1907. The headmaster, Mr. A. R. Smith, taught him each morning from 8 am to 8-45 am before the school opened at 9 am. During the winter months of 1902-4 he attended evening classes at Widnes Technical School, studying art, mathematics and physiography. Then from 1903-7 he taught at Farnworth for half of each week, attending Widnes Secondary School for the other half. The round trip from Bold to Farnworth was five miles, whilst the round trip from Bold to Widnes was eight miles. Joseph covered all these distances on foot. To quote his own words: "This period was an excellent transition between my life as an elementary school boy at Bold Heath School and that as an undergraduate."[4]

He then entered the University of Liverpool, having been awarded the Tate Technical Science entrance scholarship, and gained a First-class Honours degree in mathematics in 1910. He was then awarded an entrance exhibition to Trinity College, Cambridge, where he studied pure and applied mathematics and theoretical physics, achieving distinction in the Mathematical Tripos in 1912.

Joseph Proudman was keen to continue with research work, preferably in the field of electricity, but could not find a suitable subject to study. Instead he was referred to Professor Sir Horace Lamb, Professor of Mathematics in Manchester, who immediately set him a problem on the theory of ocean tides.[5] It was to be fifteen years before he came up with the solution, but it marked the start of his lifelong dedication to tidal research. In October 1913 he was appointed Assistant Lecturer in Mathematics at Liverpool University. He was required to give twelve lectures per week, two each morning, Monday to Saturday, and had to confine his research work to the vacations. However a research student was soon provided to assist him. The student was Arthur Doodson, who was studying at the University for his M.Sc. Joseph Proudman set him to work on electro-magnetic waves, whilst he, himself, concentrated on tides. This was the start of a lifelong association between the two scientists.

As a junior lecturer Joseph Proudman was paid an annual salary of £150 which was fixed for six years. However, in 1915 he was appointed a Fellow of Trinity College, Cambridge, which brought in a very welcome extra £350 per annum. Presumably he felt that he could now afford a wife and family because in 1916 he was married in Manchester to Rubina Ormrod, daughter of Thomas Ormrod, an insurance company manager, and they subsequently had two sons and a daughter.

Joseph Proudman was not called upon to serve in the forces in World War 1, as he was placed in a low medical category, so he remained in Liverpool, although he worked at Woolwich Arsenal for a short time in 1918 doing mathematical research into ballistics. He returned to Liverpool at the end of 1918.

Arthur Doodson

Arthur Thomas Doodson was born on 31st March 1890 at Boothstown near Worsley in Lancashire, where his father Thomas was the manager of a local cotton mill. Arthur's mother, Eleanor, was the granddaughter of Thomas Pendlebury, manufacturer of pencils in Keswick. Thomas Pendlebury's wife was related to the Barrows of Ringwood Hall, near Chesterfield, owners of the Staveley Coal and Iron Works. Arthur's grandfather, Peter Pendlebury, was a self-taught schoolmaster, who encouraged self-education in his neighbourhood, while Arthur's great-uncle, John Pendlebury, also self-taught, was Secretary of Dr. Stephenson's Orphanage, later to become the National Children's Orphanage.[5]

So it is hardly surprising that a hunger for learning was a strong characteristic of young Arthur Doodson's life. He was an avid reader. He attended the Wesleyan village school in Boothstown but found it insufficiently stimulating, so from the age of about ten, he was allowed to attend evening classes at Leigh, a few miles away, where he excelled at mathematics. His parents wanted him to become a schoolmaster, so he became a pupil-teacher at the village school, and for one year he attended the Pupil-Teachers' Centre at Leigh each morning. This was a common enough method of teacher training at the turn of the 19th/20th century.

Times were hard in the cotton industry in the early 1900s, and Arthur's father lost his job as manager of the cotton mill at Boothstown. For several months the family struggled on half wages to make ends meet, and eventually moved to Rochdale, where Mr. Doodson became manager at a local mill. For some reason he found this job "intolerable", and moved again to a rather less satisfying post as a loom overlooker.

In Rochdale Arthur continued pupil-teaching. For half of each day he attended the Rochdale Pupil -Teachers' Centre, until the centre closed down a few months later. He then studied privately for the Pupil -Teachers' exam, and attended the Rochdale Secondary School on a half-time basis. Throughout the period he studied chemistry at evening classes, this being his chosen subject at that time.

Of course Arthur was as yet unaware of the existence of Joseph Proudman, who was doing much the same thing at roughly the same time at Farnworth, not so far away.

Arthur had some musical ability, and for a time he played the organ for the Sunday School at the local Methodist Church where his parents were members.

The Doodsons raised sufficient funds to send Arthur to study at the University of Liverpool when he reached the age of 18. He was aiming for an honours degree in chemistry and physics, and at the same time he began a course at the Teachers' Training College of the University. The demands of teacher training took up so much time that he changed his second subject from physics to mathematics in the second year. In his third year he became profoundly deaf, and could hear little of what was being said at lectures. All his parents' hopes for him were shattered, but Arthur was determined not to give up. His fellow students helped out and he was permitted to use their lecture notes. He was successful in obtaining a B.Sc.1st Class in chemistry and mathematics, but had to abandon the idea of teaching due to his deafness.

He was still aiming for an honours degree, but was persuaded to specialize in mathematics rather than chemistry. He was successful a year later and was awarded the Ronald Hudson Prize for Geometry.

Even now in the 21st Century it is not easy for a disabled person to find employment, but in 1912 it was virtually impossible. Despite his high qualifications, Arthur had to settle for a post as meter-tester with Ferranti at Hollingwood, not far from Shaw, near Oldham, where the Doodson family had recently settled. Arthur did not get on particularly well with his fellow workers. His enquiring mind constantly wanted to know all the whys and wherefores of the work, whereas his workmates felt it was sufficient just to produce the output and take the wages. While at Ferranti's he signed on for an evening course in Practical Electrical Engineering at Manchester Technical College. However his poor hearing proved a problem and he soon abandoned the course.

In 1914 he moved on to work for Manchester Corporation in the Testing and Standardizing Department doing work of a semi-research nature. It involved calculations of the range and flight of projectiles. The First World War had begun, and Arthur was a conscientious objector on religious grounds. He was a member of a church community called 'The Churches of God in the Fellowship of the Son of God', previously a part of the Plymouth Brethren, and he was reluctant to do any work connected with war. War badges, accompanied by certificates signed by Lloyd George, were being distributed to indispensible members of staff, so that they could be exempted from war service. Arthur was offered one of these, but, on principle, he refused, feeling that it would be hypocritical to accept.

Whilst pursuing his daytime employment Arthur became a research student in the Department of Mathematics at the University of Liverpool working for his M.Sc. His supervisor proved to be Joseph Proudman, and Professor Carey, who held the Chair of Mathematics at the University, suggested the two meet together for two hours each Saturday morning during term time. This they did, and Arthur was initially set to work on a problem of electricity, while Joseph Proudman concentrated on the theory of tides. Arthur progressed to checking Proudman's calculations and devising related complicated formulae and mathematical tables. The tables were duly published by the British Association Committee for Mathematical Tables. He did much of the work during lunch hours and on trains and trams as he commuted between Shaw, Manchester and Liverpool. It quickly emerged that Arthur was a genius at computation, whilst Proudman was the expert on theory. For many years the two scientists were to work together.

In 1914 Doodson's work earned him his M.Sc. degree.

He found the work in Manchester did not exercise his mind sufficiently. To quote his own words: "Advancement was not rapid enough for my impatient spirit", and he was dissatisfied with engineering because "practice and experience count far, far more than technical knowledge and brain power."[6] He expressed an interest in working with the Astronomer Royal, but there were no vacancies in that field.

Meanwhile, his fiancée, Margaret Gallagher, daughter of a tramways engineer in Halifax, checked some of his calculations for him. She had been at school with Arthur in Rochdale, and had been a fellow undergraduate at the University of Liverpool. They graduated together with B.Scs.

In 1916 Arthur was called before a local tribunal to explain his reasons for wishing to avoid conscription. He wrote to Margaret: "I am the first conscientious objector in Shaw." The tribunal granted him an exemption card on the understanding that he would remain in the employ of the Manchester Corporation Electrical Department.

However, after two years he resigned his job with Manchester Corporation and took up a post at University College, London, working for Professor Karl Pearson in the Department of Applied Statistics. He asked not to be involved with war work if at all possible, but shortly afterwards the work of the department changed to ballistics in connection with the war, and Arthur was required to calculate high-angle trajectories. He was somewhat reassured when he learnt that the main purpose of his calculations was the defence of London against Zeppelins.

In a letter to Margaret, written in February 1917, he describes his new method of smoothing data values: -"I told you that Karl Pearson praised my method of smoothing. Well he took it up and got several people drawing the smoothing curves. The tables were tables of double entry and could be 'differenced' either horizontally or vertically." More than forty years later, in the 1960s, in pre-computer days, Doodson's 'differencing' methods were still being used to smooth tide tables at Bidston Observatory.

Arthur's London lodgings were at 53 Guilford Street, Russell Square. Here he experienced the air raids at first hand. On September 18th 1917 he described the raid as "the worst so far - a great deal of damage to life and property. The West Central Hotel seriously damaged by a bomb. Southampton Row badly damaged - much loss of life. Bombs fell in Grays Inn Road (at the other end of Guilford Street)." He commented on the raids of February 19th 1918, when the

Midland Hotel near St. Pancras was hit - a pinnacle fell down and killed several people. Arthur tried joining the crowds in the tube station, but found it was impossible to move about on the platform, and the atmosphere was "far from wholesome", so he returned to his lodgings. His deafness enabled him to sleep through much of the air raid!

The only damage to University College itself was caused by an unexploded bomb making a hole 5 to 6 feet deep in the lawn.

At this time Professor Pearson gave up his post and Arthur Doodson took charge of the Anti-Aircraft Gunnery Branch of the Munitions Inventions Department (M.I.D.). They were still working on gun trajectories, and at that time the department was working from two rooms at the top of a high building at Queen Anne's Gate. In fine weather the staff took tea out on the roof, enjoying the views of the London sky-line, and some of the ladies (or "computers" as he was to call his junior staff throughout his working life) chose to work out there. For the first time Arthur had responsibility for the hiring of staff and the running of the department. There was quite a turnover of staff as people went off to enlist. His experience would stand him in good stead in future years at Bidston.

In 1918 Proudman made the first suggestion that Arthur might like to work with him on tidal matters. However the war continued, and nobody knew how many more years it would last!

Arthur wrote several papers, which were used in the 'Text-book of Anti-Aircraft Gunnery', published in 1925. This became a standard manual on the subject. At this time

Margaret was giving an instructional course to engineers on the use of slide rules. Arthur commented on how expensive slide rules now were - 30 shilling each - and suggested to Margaret that she design paper slide rules which could be cut up. She may well have done so, because paper slide rules were in regular use in analysis work at Bidston right up to the 1960s.

In September 1918 the department moved once again, this time to Broad Sanctuary Chambers. Members of staff were still volunteering for the war effort. However all this was to change in November. Arthur was standing in front of Westminster Abbey when a maroon was fired at 11 a.m. on November 11th to mark the end of the war. He reported to Margaret that: "There were wild scenes, the streets rapidly filled and by 12 o'clock Whitechapel, the Mall and Trafalgar Square were sights to behold - everybody seemed to be joyriding and going mad generally."

The end of the war brought an end to the need for ballistic calculations. Although Arthur was instructed to continue running the office normally, he advised his staff "to take whatever suitable appointments came along." Of his own future he said "I cannot consent to becoming a mere money-making machine. I have no desire to "boss" and care not how many people are over me so long as I am free to carry out my own ideas as much as possible."
A short time later Proudman asked him if he would be interested in taking up tidal work at a salary of £300 or £350 per year. The answer was an emphatic yes - he would even be prepared to take a monetary loss. There were plans to set up

a Geodetic Institute in England. Proudman, now Professor of Mathematics at the University of Liverpool, thought that this Institute, if it went ahead at all, would be likely to be split up. If so, he would ask for the Tidal Department to go to Liverpool where he was confident the local shipowners would provide financial support. He was proved correct in this. Charles Booth, Chairman of the Booth Steamship Company, pronounced it "a capital idea." Professor Proudman hoped to engage a really capable man as secretary of the new Tidal Institute. This man would run the Institute, and Professor Proudman would only have a nominal involvement. Arthur Doodson would be the ideal person to fill the post. Arthur was offered a salary of £350 per year, financed by Alfred Booth, whilst Charles Booth would cover the other running costs of the Institute. He accepted the offer, after declining an invitation from Professor Pearson to remain at University College. For a number of years Arthur and Margaret had shelved the idea of marriage. Arthur, describing himself as an "unsentimental brute", felt it was better to wait a few years in order to have "champagne and oysters" rather than "cockles and pop"! By 1919 the time had come. His staff at University College had been moved to Woolwich. He went with them and stayed for a few weeks - long enough to see them settled in. He resigned at the end of March, and in mid-April he and Margaret were married. He was 29 and she was 26. In the same year he was awarded the degree of D.Sc. by Liverpool University for a thesis on ballistics, and he was appointed Secretary of the newly founded Tidal Institute.

Chapter Fifteen

The One O'clock Gun

As indicated in Chapter Five, the move from the Liverpool side of the river was instrumental in bringing into being the use of a time gun which could be heard on both sides of the river. In January 1867 a report from the Marine Surveyor recommended that a system of "firing by clock work, to be controlled from the Observatory by electricity" should be adopted.[1] Messrs James Ritchie and Sons of Edinburgh estimated the work would cost £20 to £25. A cannon from the Crimea War was obtained and set up at Morpeth Dock in Birkenhead. A shelter was built for the use of the operator, and the gun was sited on the roof of the structure (see photo).

The postcard shows the cannon at Morpeth Dock at the turn of the 19th Century.

A landline was laid from the Observatory to Morpeth Dock, and a clock, installed in the shelter and connected to the gun, was controlled by landline from the normal clock in the Observatory. A stage hand primed the gun ready for firing, and careful time checks were made by landline to the Observatory staff. At one second to one o'clock the operator at Bidston flicked a switch, the circuit was completed and the cannon fired at precisely one p.m.

The first firing of the gun took place on September 21st 1867. Rumour has it that seven pounds of gunpowder were used on this first occasion. The resulting explosion blew out windows on both sides of the river. Subsequently five pounds of powder were used.

The dropping of the time ball at the Waterloo Dock Observatory was unavoidably discontinued a few months before the firing of the gun started at Bidston. During the interval GMT was supplied daily to a "large number of persons who brought chronometers to Bidston to obtain their errors."

The procedure for the firing of the gun was unchanged for many years, until, in 1898, Mr. Plummer, the Director at that time, suggested that the gun be controlled directly from the normal clock at the Observatory, eliminating the need to involve the clock at Morpeth Dock in the circuit. The latter clock used very large batteries, which caused blackening at the contact points and gave rise to frequent cleaning. The new system was approved and duly implemented. A galvanometer, connected by cable to the gun, was also installed at the Observatory - "so we know if it (the gun) has gone off on windy or foggy days." There had presumably been total reliance on eyes and ears up to that time. The gunner stood by ready to step in and fire the gun manually if the signal from Bidston failed.

The gun was fired every day apart from Sundays at exactly 1 p.m. GMT, so in summer the gun was fired at 2 p.m. local time. There was an extra firing at 2400 hours on 31st December 1900 to mark the start of the new century - note the year was 1900 - not 1899.

On an anniversary of Armistice Day, Nov 11th 1918, the gun was to be fired at four seconds before 11a.m., so that the sound would reach Liverpool at 11 a.m. precisely. Advance information was sent to all the local press. This procedure was adopted as an annual event, although which year it had started is not recorded.

Details in the University of Liverpool archives, dating from the foundation of the Tidal Institute in 1919, show that, at that time, the University paid for the gunpowder, which came from W. H. Wakefield & Co. Ltd. The gun used up about one barrel per month. This was priced at £3 in 1929. Powder fuses were 11/4d per month from Christopher & Company and other requirements were flannelette, thread, needles, twine, mops and brooms costing £3-19-3d.[2]

The stage-hand firing the gun at Morpeth Dock was paid £1-19-0d. I can't find many entries of this. Was that the pay for a whole year? As the stage-hands were employed by the Mersey Docks and Harbour Board (MDHB), the University paid their wages via the treasurer of the MDHB.

The old gun gradually developed signs of ageing. In August 1928 the gun carriage broke and in September the axle of the front wheels broke "due to wear and tear." The gun was removed and replaced by a spare. The estimated cost of repair to the carriage was £14, and the gun had to be revented by the Army Ordnance Depot at Burscough at a cost of £10.

An order sent to Bidston on March 25th 1930, from the Master, Boards Stages, gives us some idea of the equipment required at the gunsite:-
"The Secretary, LOTI
Please supply -
50 yards flannelette (to make powder bags)
2 reels thread (18 white)
1 packet needles (18)
3 lbs mop thrums
2 balls twine
1 iron bucket"

In 1932 the Army Ordnance Depot at Burscough finally condemned the gun, and the Marine Committee of the Dock Board wanted to take the opportunity to abolish the firing after Armistice Day that year. It was no longer thought necessary, as BBC time signals had been available since 1925. However, the proposal met with strong dissent and the decision was postponed for three months. Meanwhile the Daily Post and Echo offered to meet the cost of a new cannon, but the War Office offered a 32 pounder from Woolwich Arsenal at a "trifling" cost. This was accepted, the Marine Committee's proposal was abandoned, and the annual firing of the gun on Armistice Day continued until it was brought to a halt by the Second World War. The new gun came into use in April 1933.

Generally speaking the firing of the one o'clock gun was on time each day, and the Bidston annual reports suggest that only a handful of days were missed in any one year.

However there was the occasional mishap:-
Letter from the Associate Director (Dr. Doodson) to the Secretary of the Dock Board, Dec. 28th 1932:
"I have to report that on Saturday last, Dec 24th, the Time Gun was fired late; the firing switch here was closed at the correct time, 12.59, but no firing signal being received from the gunner, was kept closed until 10 seconds after 13.00. At 5 seconds after 13.01 the usual O.K. signal was received from the gunner. The signal received here appears to indicate that the gun was fired one minute late; the gunner's sole statement to us is that his watch had stopped, and the gun was fired two seconds late. This does not seem consistent with the facts as stated here, and I shall be obliged if you will take the matter up."

Reply from Dock Office - Jan 2nd 1933:-
"Dear Sir,
Delay in firing of Time Gun - Saturday, 24th Dec, 1932
Referring to your letter of the 29th Ultimo, hereon-
The gunner states that after the time signals for checking the gun clock had been completed at noon on the above date, he proceeded to the gun which he loaded and got ready by about 12.45 p.m.
He then had to wait until 10 seconds before 1.0 p.m. when he had to be in the clock house in order to complete the electrical firing circuit between Bidston and the gun.
Whilst waiting he looked at his watch, which showed 12.50

p.m., but he did not notice that it had stopped until he heard the first of the chimes of the clock at the Birkenhead Town Hall.

He then rushed out of the gun house up to the clock house where he completed the circuit and fired the gun himself by the auxiliary circuit being, as he thought, only a few seconds late and not one minute.

Yours faithfully,

F.W.Mace, Capt.R.N.R.,Marine Surveyor and Water Bailiff.'

(As on previous occasions I note that this flurry of correspondence occurred around Christmas time, suggesting that the Director at Bidston took very short Christmas holidays).

On March 13th, 1933 the gun failed to fire - this was blamed on defective fuses. These were returned to the suppliers (Christopher and Co. of Wigan) on 28th March, who sent them back to the makers asking for an explanation. The makers claimed that the fuses were very old stock which must have been supplied by accident.

However it is interesting to note that these problems arose while the old Crimea cannon was still awaiting replacement. The new 32 pounder was brought into use in April 1933, and no more problems were recorded.

The old cannon was placed on the Observatory lawn near the lych-gate giving access to the hill.

On Tuesday 28th January 1936 the gun was fired at 1-30 p.m. to indicate the commencement of two minutes silence to mark the funeral of King George V.

A security silence which lasted six and a half years was imposed from September 1939 and the firing of the gun ceased. Following the end of the Second World War it was proposed to resume the one o'clock firing. This time a six pounder naval Hotchkiss anti-aircraft gun was provided, and the firing resumed in June 1946. To avoid confusion over GMT the gun was fired at 1 p.m. clock time from then onwards.

In 1948 the gun carriage on the lawn needed repairs at a cost of £20, and in 1951 Dr. Doodson reported that one side of this gun carriage had been eaten away by dry rot. This was presumably fixed.

In the 1960s the responsibility of overseeing the firing of the gun fell to the landing stage dockmaster who was on day duty for that week. Stan Amos of Moreton remembers it well. He operated from Monday-Friday, and was paid six pence a day (i.e. 2/6 per week). This came as a small supplement to his wage as a landing stage hand, and the duty came round about one week in six.

The daily charge of 14 ounces of powder (not the 5 pounds of a century earlier) was put in a linen type bag. The gunpowder came by rail from Pembroke to the goods yard at Morpeth Dock and was delivered once a month in barrels. This suggests that each barrel would contain about 20 pounds of powder.

The test firing took place at 12-30, the girl at Bidston flicking the switch. If nothing happened at Morpeth, i.e. there was a fault on the line, the stage-hand had to run to the nearest telephone, which was at the Wallasey cattle station, and ring Bidston. At 12-55 he loaded up the gun powder, and if the firing from Bidston at 1 pm failed to trigger the gun, he used a stick to trigger the mechanism within a second or two.

There was no heating in the hut, and it was very cold at times. The whole procedure, including washing the gun with soda water and preparing it for the next day, took a whole hour, and all for the grand sum of sixpence! The gun was painted once a year.

There was a clock in the hut, very accurate and resembling the one at Bidston. These two clocks had of course to be identical in timing.

The gun was fired for the last time on 20th July 1969. It is survived by the One o'clock Gun at Edinburgh Castle, which is still fired regularly.

The above photo shows the gun, apparently the 32-pounder, still in place at Morpeth Dock in 2004. It has been maintained in good condition.
A ferry terminal now lies between Morpeth Dock and Liverpool.

Chapter Sixteen

Astronomy

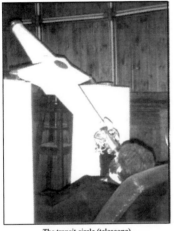

The transit circle (telescope)
(Courtesy National Museums Liverpool)

The first telescopes, a transit circle and an equatorial telescope, were set up at the Waterloo Dock Observatory on the Liverpool waterfront in 1845. The main objective was the calculation of accurate time for Liverpool, and the transit telescope was used to do this by observing stars as they passed directly overhead. The equatorial telescope was used to observe comets.

The Waterloo Dock Observatory had one dome, under which the equatorial telescope was housed. The transit telescope was housed behind a wooden shutter at first floor level, to the left of the dome. Immediately behind this was a mast on which the time ball was mounted.

The astronomical aspect of the Observatory was not without its critics. For instance, on March 7th 1845 the Liverpool

Mercury reported that a new comet had been noted by the High School Observatory of Philadelphia on Jan. 26th. The following comment was made -

"The wretched situation of the Liverpool Observatory has precluded the chance of the comet being discerned from that station, however plainly it may be seen elsewhere. The instruments might as well be in a Wapping cellar as where they are." (Originator of the comment not named). There was also concern that proximity to the river might result in waves shaking the telescopes and making their use difficult. However this proved not to be the case as the mounting was so sturdy.

In fact the Liverpool equatorial was considered to be the finest instrument in existence for daylight observation of small planets and comets as they crossed the meridian. The Greenwich Observatory had not as yet acquired a comparable instrument, so it was arranged that, for the time being, Liverpool would take the responsibility for observing faint planets and comets, specifically those between the orbits of Mars and Jupiter.

A sample extract from a letter from Mr. Hartnup to the Royal Astronomical Society (RAS) reads:
"On the 15th September (1847) we had here one of those superb nights with which we are so seldom favoured. I never before saw Saturn so beautifully defined. The main division in the bright ring was steadily seen in every part, except where the ring was hid by the belt of the planet. Bond's ring could not be overlooked for an instant. The new ring is much broader than represented by Professor Bond and Mr. Dawes

when first discovered. It occupies full half, or from half to two-thirds of the space between the inner bright ring, and fades away as it approaches the ball of the planet."[1]

There was close collaboration between Liverpool and Greenwich, and in 1849 Mr. Hartnup's observation of comets and planets allowed Greenwich and Cambridge to concentrate on other work whilst their new equatorial was being constructed, but Greenwich took over the observation of comets when they were too low in the sky for the Liverpool equatorial to observe.

The Liverpool Observatory was held in great esteem by the Astromomer Royal and by astronomers throughout Europe. A quote from the Annual report of the Council of the RAS, published in February 1852 says, "Of the Liverpool Observatory nothing new need be said; it maintains its reputation as the most trustworthy for extra-meridional observations, for immediate use. The excellence of his equatorial enables Mr. Hartnup to compare all his objects with one or more perfectly well-determined stars, so that he obtains at once what an Observatory less completely equipped (that is, almost every other Observatory) may wait months to obtain."[2]

In 1851 John Hartnup planned to observe the eclipse of the sun, but was only able to monitor the beginning and end of the event. The weather was unfavourable most of the time.

Mr. Hartnup suffered from a period of severe illness during the latter part of May 1852, which left him in "such a state of debility as to render it highly imprudent for me to expose myself to the night air, to any great extent, during June and July." Consequently night-time observations with the equatorial were discontinued during this period. (Presumably the assistant, John Shearer, was not a sufficiently experienced astronomer or was not on the premises at night). By August 24th, however, every department of the Observatory was again in full activity.

When the new Observatory was erected on Bidston Hill in 1864 it was furnished with two domes, the one on the eastern side was used to house the transit telescope and the western one housed the equatorial.

Both domes could revolve through 360 degrees (and can still do so in the 21st century). An aperture about two feet wide could be exposed as part of the dome roof slid upwards and backwards (rather like a 1950s pencil case). Thus the telescopes could be turned and pointed at the open sky in any direction.

In the latter half of 1909 and into 1910 Halley's Comet was observed, but "persistent cloudy weather prevented it being seen at its greatest brilliance", while in 1912 the eclipse of the sun in April was "well-observed."

Observations made with the transit telescope for the determination of time had continued from 1845 right through the turn of the century. During the First World War night-time observations posed a problem. To quote Mr. Plummer in 1916 "the police regulations for obscuring artificial light have

greatly interfered with the extra-meridial observations."
As radio telegraphy gradually took over, and it was now
possible to obtain time signals from Greenwich, the need for
the transit observations was fading. However, for several
years observations with the transit were continued alongside
the radio time signals, presumably as an additional check.
The last reference I can find is in the annual report of 1921.

As industry developed so the atmosphere became polluted,
and this, together with increasing use of electric light, meant
that conditions for the operation of telescopes were becoming
less favourable. The telescopes fell into disuse, although an
invoice dated July 3rd 1935 shows that Charles Jones and
Sons of Claughton, Birkenhead, were called in to paint the
equatorial and transit telescopes at a total cost of £5-9-0d.
The transit was moved to Liverpool Museum in the late
1950s.

Some years later, in 1960, members of the Liverpool University
Astronomical Society were given permission to use the
equatorial telescope, provided they clean it up and maintain
it. Although they found the instrument to be "mounted on
a most elaborate equatorial mounting, and equipped with
a fine selection of eyepieces, micrometers and other items
including a spectroscope", the telescope was in a "sorry
state" with "many layers of thick paint now covering the once
proud brasswork." The work kept the Society members busy
for many an afternoon. The University Fabrics Department
re-covered the floor, while an engineer was hired to check
the mechanism of the mounting and the drive. The optical
instruments were overhauled, cleaned and polished by the

University Optics Department, who were also responsible for dissolving the paint off and polishing the brasswork. There is a story that a builder, who was hired to weatherproof the dome, had not been informed about the two foot wide opening aperture across the apex of the dome. He assumed the two long cracks extending right over the dome were the cause of rain getting in, and he duly filled them up with putty. Members of the Society were subsequently unable to open the slit, and the builder had to undo all his hard work.[3]

Although the Society was very happy with the newly refurbished telescope, its use does not seem to have lasted for more than a few years, for the telescope was removed from Bidston and put on display in Liverpool Museum in 1969.

Chapter Seventeen

The Lord Kelvin Tide Predicting Machine

(An extract from the paper "How Science Aids Port Navigation - Liverpool and Tidal Research" prepared by Dr. A.T. Doodson for the "Mersey" magazine - Volume 5 - July 1927.)

A Short Description

It may be of interest to consider how the tides are predicted. The Tide Predicting Machine is here illustrated.

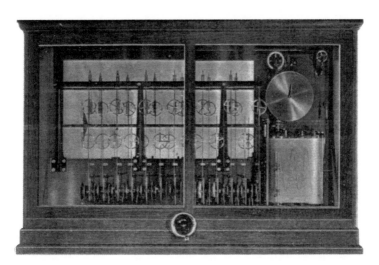

It stands about seven feet high, is six feet long and two feet wide, and is encased by sliding glass doors. The principles of the machine are not difficult to understand. Suppose that the main shaft revolves once per solar day and drives a number of gears which operate a number of cranks, and that these cranks can be made to give, at any point of their length, vertical motions to rods carrying pulleys in a vertical plane. A wire passes alternately over and under the pulleys and carries an index at its free end; then, as the main shaft revolves, the pulleys move up and down and the index registers the total motion. We have, further, a drum connected to the main shaft so that each revolves once per solar day, and a pen is attached to the free end of the wire. As the drum revolves it unrolls a roll of paper from one container to another and needle-points on the edges of the drum pierce the paper at intervals of an hour. The pen moves up and down as the drum revolves, and the result is a curve from which one can read the heights of the pen at any moment of the day.

The Mechanism Explained

Now let us consider the relations of the motions of the pulleys to the oscillations of the tide. The most important set of gears and pulleys make the pen to rise and fall in a period of 12h. 25m., and if the throw of the crank can be arranged so as to give on a suitable scale a range of 20 feet with the highest point of the pen about 11 hours after the moon crosses the meridian, then we shall get a curve giving a fairly close approximation to the tidal motion at Liverpool. When once set the machine could go on predicting this approximation to the Liverpool tide for as many years as required. Of course since one revolution of the drum corresponds to one solar day we can speed up the machine so as to make it complete a year's curve in four hours. The apparatus can be arranged so as to give any required throw of the crank, and for High Water of each constituent to be given at any required time, so that the machine can thus be used for any port.

But it is necessary to get much better predictions than are here indicated, and for this purpose there are 26 sets of gears and pulleys all working together at the same time. One set acting alone would give High Water at intervals of exactly twelve hours and, whereas the former set would give the principal part of the tide caused by the moon, the latter set would give the principal part of the tide caused by the sun. For this second constituent the range of motion contributed to the pen and the time of High Water can be set according to the amounts ascertained previously, as pertaining to the port for which the machine is being used. Thus a range of six feet and High Water at noon would be appropriate for Liverpool.

Now consider the pulleys acting together. If, for Liverpool, the moon crosses the meridian about 1 a.m., then both sets of pulleys will act together on the pen and the total range will be 26 feet (20 feet plus 6 feet). But seven days later the lunar constituent would tend to give High Water when the solar one was tending to give Low Water, and the result of their opposition would be a range of only 14 feet (20 feet minus 6 feet). Hence the machine would draw a curve which would give large 'spring' tides and small 'neap' tides, as they are called. Similarly we could trace the effects of a constituent which would give increased tidal range when an increased attractive force is caused by the moon being nearer to the earth and decreased range when the moon is far away.

Other pulleys cause (represent?) alterations in the height of successive tides due to the moon's attractive forces varying with her distance north or south of the equator.

A large number of variations in the motions and attractive forces of the sun and moon are known, and the most important of these find their counterpart on the machine.

General Observations

The settings of the machine can only be performed when actual tides have been analysed for the data required for each set of gears, and elaborate tables are then available to help in setting the machine for any subsequent or previous date. When once set the machine is allowed to run for the equivalent of a year's tides and is then re-set as required.

The methods of analysis call for much research and the problems are of a very complicated nature, but progress is being made continuously and the needs of commerce are being met, in this respect as in others, by Liverpool enterprise.

Chapter Eighteen

Meteorology

William Hutchinson, Liverpool Dockmaster 1759-1801, was keen to make meteorological observations as well as tidal ones, so, at the Old Dock Gates in Liverpool, he took note of wind velocity and compass direction, the barometric pressure reading at noon solar time, and the temperature of the air at 8 a.m. (His thermometer was sited at the head of a staircase four storeys high - this would hardly be acceptable in modern times). He also made notes on rainfall and current weather conditions, and published four volumes of "Hutchinson's Journals of Observations of Tides and Weather taken at the Old Dock Gates, Liverpool", covering the period 1768-1793.

It seems that no-one was keen enough to continue this work after he died in 1801, although the need for weather observations was a leading factor in the setting up of the Waterloo Dock Observatory in 1844.

It had been pointed out by Lieutenant Jones in 1837 in his first appeal for an Observatory to be set up in Liverpool, that there was need for vessels preparing to leave the Mersey to be given warning of approaching storms, as "too many vessels are lost when they are unprepared for such events."

Several recent disasters would have given weight to his argument:-

On December 3rd 1823 there was noted "a very violent hurricane", in which several vessels were blown on shore in Bootle Bay and other parts of the river. The comment was that "more serious accidents happened from this storm than from any other since the memorable one in the year 1560" - Gore's Annals tell us merely that in 1560 "The haven (presumably the harbour at Liverpool) was destroyed by a storm."[1]

In 1833 a severe storm had resulted in a storm surge 8.5 feet above the predicted tide level, and in 1839 a very severe storm caused enormous damage to shipping and on land on Sunday, January 6th.[2] The storm lasted two days, during which time the Bidston Telegraph was broken down. Sandbanks and beaches were strewn with wreckage, and four ships - the Brighton, the Pennsylvania, the Lockwoods, and the St. Andrew all ran aground. The Pennsylvania and St. Andrew were New York packet ships outward bound, while the Lockwoods was an emigrant ship carrying 108 people. The steam tug Victoria, assisted by the Magazines lifeboat, managed to rescue 55 people from the Lockwoods, 26 from the Pennsylvania and 23 from the St. Andrew. The Brighton, inward bound from Bombay, ran on to a sandbank and 14 of the crew were drowned while attempting to reach shore on a raft.

During this storm the old mill on Grange Hill, West Kirby, was blown down.[3] This mill had featured on charts for over 200 years and was still an aid to navigation. In 1840 the Sub-Committee for the Department of the Marine Surveyor was provided with an estimate for "the probable cost of erecting a Sea Mark 120 feet high near the site of the Grange Mill in Cheshire, which is now taken down."[4] After consideration the Committee resolved that "the Dock Surveyor be requested to furnish an estimate of the cost of a rough stone column not exceeding 60 feet high and also of the cost of a mark of wood of the same height." In 1841 the stone Beacon pillar (still standing in 2006) was erected for the benefit of mariners "frequenting the Mersey and its vicinity." Rumour had it that a rock chamber full of human bones was found under the mill during excavation.

The severity of this storm may well have been a decisive factor in convincing the Liverpool Town Council of the necessity for an Observatory, because only a few months later they gave the go-ahead for the Astronometrical Observatory to be set up in Liverpool and one of the principle duties of Mr. Hartnup and his assistant was to observe the weather.

The meteorological instruments were supplied by Mr. Adie and included a standard barometer of Newman's construction, a rain gauge of Howard's construction, a maximum and a minimum thermometer and wet and dry bulb thermometers. The first meteorological observations were made on October 1st 1845. There is no mention of an anemometer being included at that stage, although by January 1849, in his report to the Observatory Committee, John Hartnup noted that the direction and force of the wind were recorded daily. Presumably they were purely visual estimates, for in August of that year Mr. Hartnup expressed a wish for an anemometer which could record the wind force and direction. However this would have cost a prohibitive £60 and Hartnup's request seems not to have been acceded to until December 1851 when an Osler's anemometer, designed by Mr. Follett Osler, with an associated pluviometer (rain recorder) was installed. This means that the rain gauge was of necessity sited on the roof of the Observatory, about 30 feet above the ground. This would not have met with the approval of the future Meteorological Office, which stipulates that rain gauges must always be sited at ground level. Cloud details were also noted.

The observations were initially made at two o'clock Gottingen mean solar time, which, according to Mr. Hartnup, was one of the hours fixed upon for recording such observations in all public meteorological and magnetic observatories (Gottingen, in Germany, had an important astronomical observatory sited at its university).

In December 1851, John Hartnup was clearly delighted by the acquisition of the Osler's 'improved' anemometer which cost £160 - he does not tell us where the money came from. The instrument was apparently very large by modern standards. The working mechanisms were connected to pens which recorded the information on a paper chart. The pluviometer recorded details of starting and stopping times of precipitation, together with its rate of fall, by drawing a line on an analogue chart. Records show that the pluviometer was still being used to determine times of precipitation as late as 1920.

The Registrar-General was receiving weekly weather statistics, referred to as 'daily conditions of the atmosphere', from the Astronomer-Royal, and the Liverpool Health Committee requested that similar reports be provided by John Hartnup to the Medical Officer of Health in Liverpool. These reports were duly provided, and were included in the Quarterly Register of Mortality in England. They commenced in 1849, and were still being provided 150 years later. Details of temperature, atmospheric pressure and relative humidity were made available.

The Royal Astronomical Society had some concern that their Astronomer was being distracted by his meteorological duties. To quote their Annual Report of 1852: "Mr. Hartnup has lately been charged with the duty of taking very extended meteorological observations, at the request of the Registrar-General. We are rejoiced to find researches and observations of so useful a nature in such good hands; but we trust that Mr. Hartnup's patrons will not forget that, after having gained the applause of the astronomical world for the liberality and judgment with which they planned and furnished their Observatory and after the striking success by which it has been attended, it would be bad economy to divert the principal attention of their astronomer from astronomy."[5]

Mr. Hartnup responded by pointing out that he had an assistant (John Shearer) who had been with him since 1847, and who was now so well acquainted with the routine duties of the Observatory that, between them, they could get through a much larger quantity of work than in earlier years.

GENERAL REMARKS.

8th. Cumuli nearly covered the sky till 1 p.m., the amount of cloud was very variable during the afternoon and evening; the mean being about four-tenths; cumuli and cirri. There were several light showers of rain in the morning.

9th. About seven-tenths of the sky were covered with cirro-cumuli throughout the day. Lightning, thunder, and heavy rain between 10 and 11 a.m.

10th. The sky was overcast till 3 p.m., after which the clouds were broken; cumuli and cirro-cumuli. Heavy rain fell between 5 and 7 a.m., and lightning was seen and thunder heard between 7 and 8 p.m.

11th. The sky was overcast throughout the day; cumulo-strati. Steady rain fell from 10½ a.m., to 1½ p.m., and there were several showers during the afternoon and evening.

12th. Cumuli and cumulo-strati covered the sky throughout the day, rain fell from 10½ a.m., to 1 p.m., and there were several very heavy showers during the afternoon. Lightning was seen and thunder heard between 3 and 5 p.m.

13th. About five-tenths of the sky were covered with cumuli till 2 p.m., for the remainder of the day it was clear.

14th. Lightning was seen and thunder heard between 3 and 4 a.m., and there was a heavy shower of rain between 7 and 8 a.m. The clouds were broken, from noon to 3 p.m., with this exception, the sky was overcast throughout the day; cumuli and cirro-cumuli.

THE NOMENCLATURE FOR THE CLOUDS, USED IN THE REMARKS, IS THAT FIRST PROPOSED BY MR. LUKE HOWARD, UNDER THE FOLLOWING HEADS :—

1. CIRRUS.—*A cloud resembling a lock of hair, or a feather. Parallel, flexuous, or diverging fibres, unlimited in the direction of their increase.*
2. CUMULUS.—*A cloud which increases from above, dense, convex, or conical heaps.*
3. STRATUS.—*An extended, continuous level sheet of cloud, increasing from beneath.*
4. CIRRO-CUMULUS.—*A connected system of small roundish clouds, placed in close order or contact.*
5. CIRRO-STRATUS.—*A horizontal or slightly inclined sheet, attenuated at its circumference, concave downward, or undulated.*
6. CUMULO-STRATUS.—*A cloud in which the structure of the cumulus is mixed with that of the cirro-stratus, or cirro-cumulus.*
7. NIMBUS.—*A dense cloud, spreading out into a crown of cirrus, and passing beneath into a shower.*

J. HARTNUP.

August 1852

The chart on the preceding page shows part of a weekly weather report sent to the Registrar General in August 1852. Note the use of Latin plurals in the cloud descriptions, and that, unusually for Merseyside, thunderstorms were recorded on four of the seven days.

In 1862 a "self registering barometer", designed by Alfred King, a notable engineer and inventor, of the Liverpool United Gaslight Company, and built by a local firm, J. G. Lancaster, under the close supervision of Mr. King, was installed at the Observatory. Its design was simple (see photo) - a green cylinder floated in a circular tank of mercury. As the mercury expanded and contracted due to the variation in atmospheric pressure, the drum moved up and down and a pen attached to it recorded the movement on a chart on a rotating drum. By modern standards the barograph was very large - about 2.5 metres high and about 1.5 metres wide.

King's Barograph
(Courtesy National Museums Merseyside)

The King's barograph was moved to the new Observatory on Bidston Hill in 1866, and continued in use till 1928, when it was replaced by a second King's barograph. The second instrument became inefficient in 1940, and was replaced by a micro-barograph from Short and Mason. The original barograph is on display in the World Museum, and its successor was accepted for display at the Science Museum in South Kensington, London.

(Both the Osler's anemometer and the King's barograph were described in detail by G. Reynolds in his paper 'Weather records at the Liverpool Observatory' published in "Weather", August 1954).

The recording of meteorological data at the new Observatory on Bidston Hill started in earnest on January 1st 1867. Bidston has a continuous record of temperature and rainfall from that time up to quite recently.

This Robinson Cup Anemometer, at Armagh Observatory, was renovated in 2001.
(Photograph by permission of Professor Bailey, Director of Armagh Observatory).

Wind observations were greatly improved by the installation of a Robinson's cup anemometer (see photo) at Bidston in the late 1860s, and average velocity between any hour and the hour following could now be measured. The Robinson had been invented in 1846 by Dr. Thomas Romney Robinson of Armagh Observatory.

The height of the Bidston Instrument was 56 feet above the ground, and 251 feet above sea level.

On 12th December 1883 John Hartnup Junior reported that: "From midnight to 1 a.m. on the 12th a velocity of 92 miles was recorded. On one other occasion only since the erection of this instrument in 1867 has this extreme been reached."

A letter written by William Plummer in the 1890s gives us some insight into the workings of the Robinson anemometer:-

"Report on Wind Observations
The form of anemometer employed is that known as the Robinson consisting of four hemispherical cups mounted at the end of arms and of known lengths, supported on a vertical axis and turned by the wind on a fixed pivot. The number of resolutions of the arms and cups is practically registered on a revolving drum conveniently placed beneath and it is assumed that a certain number of rotations indicate the horizontal motion of the atmosphere through a definite distance.
Simultaneously, a pressure plate records by the displacement of springs, the force the wind exerts on one square foot of area.
Evidently there should be an easily recognizable law connecting the pressure and the velocity. Such a law is not recognizable in the records maintained by the Board ...."

However Plummer was beginning to have some doubts about the accuracy of the Robinson anemometer. In February 1896 he wrote to W. H. Dines Esq. reporting that he "had been struck with the frequent record of high velocities and particularly high pressures (on the square foot) to have mistrusted in some measure the accuracy of our records." Mr. Dines replied that in his opinion "no plate that oscillates could be depended upon to give the maximum (reading) correctly". This response is hardly surprising, coming as it did from a designer of anemometers. However it procured a sale for Mr. Dines, for a few weeks later the Marine Committee instructed Mr. Plummer to investigate the possibility of installing a Dines Pressure Tube anemometer at Bidston. He inspected the Meteorological Council's Dines anemometer at their station in Holyhead, and eventually an instrument was purchased from Munros of King's Cross, London and installed at Bidston at a cost of £26-5-0s.

William Plummer was delighted with the new anemometer which was set up on the roof cabin. To quote his words - It was "simple in construction - not likely to get out of order. Moreover it possesses the additional advantage of requiring no wheel work or gearing which may become clogged by dirt or worn by use. In order to diminish the effect of the eddies arising from the form of the buildings beneath, the vane, with the tubes attached, has been carried ten feet higher than the older anemometers (Robinson and Osler)."

Dines Pressure Tube Anemometer – the area exposed on the roof was quite small.

The Dines anemometer continued in use until 1928, when it was replaced by a more up-to-date Dines model presented to the Observatory by Mr. C. Livingston. This anemometer was in continuous use for more than 60 years, until it was replaced by an automatic wind recorder in the late 1990s!

So for more than twenty years, from 1896, three wind recorders were in use, the Osler, the Robinson and the Dines. Correlation between the latter two proved difficult; and this may have been partly due to the large size of the Robinson - the diameter of the hemispherical cups was eight inches, whilst the 'radius from centre to axis of rotation' was 28.65 inches. During a severe storm on November 28th 1897, the arms of the Robinson were 'carried away', but the Dines was undamaged due to its much smaller exposed area. (The Robinson was, however, repaired within two weeks).

Dines Pressure Tube Anemometer - recording wind speed and direction on an analogue chart.

An order placed with Jones J. Hicks, Esq. of Hatton Gardens, London, in the 1880s, for "thermometers on porcelain scales in copper cases", conjures up an interesting picture of Victorian instruments.

In 1895 the Medical Officer of Health asked if sunshine records could be made available. Presumably the cost of a sunshine recorder was prohibitive, for it was not until late 1907 that a Campbell Stokes sunshine recorder was kindly provided by Mr. Eric Robson. Regular measurement of sunshine began on January 1st 1908.

An experimental series of daily forecasts of meteorological effects on the sea level at Liverpool was introduced at Bidston in late 1923: the forecasts combined information from the Air Ministry with the tidal predictions for Liverpool.

(L. T. I.'s predictions of tides for Liverpool had just been started). The Air Ministry information consisted of a coded telegram of weather data recorded at 1pm, plus forecasts of wind and barometric pressure. This was sent between 3.30 and 4 p.m. at a cost of 2/6d for a single forecast and one shilling for the coded telegram. It was quickly realized that weather data was needed more than once a day, so the Observatory's first radio receiver, assembled in the physics department of the University of Liverpool, was installed at Bidston. A member of staff, Norman C. Hobbs, was to 'train himself in the receiving of such messages and in the construction of corresponding synoptic charts'. For the additional responsibility he would receive an extra five shillings a week. In July 1926 this was increased to ten shillings a week. This was in payment for "producing forecasts of meteorological effects on sea level together with the associated forecasts of barometer and wind." This may have begun to give rise to Bidston's reputation as a weather forecasting station - a belief which still survived into the 1990s! (See page 310).

Shortly after this Dr. Doodson requested that a morse recorder be installed at the Observatory. In a memo to the Dock Board he said:

"At the present time the Observatory has no assistant who can be regarded as at all expert in the reception of Morse Messages. It is highly desirable that the Observatory shall be in a position to receive the synopses of meteorological observations over the British Isles and the Eastern Atlantic Ocean, sent out by wireless one hour after the observations have been recorded. With this information available the Observatory would be able to deduce meteorological forecasts, as required. This ought to be regarded as an essential part of the work of the Observatory.

In connection with this, we have been asked if we could supply trial forecasts to Alfred Holt and Co., and we have agreed to do what we can for them.

I have visited Stonyhurst College Observatory to inspect their apparatus, and I am of the opinion that we cannot do better than to purchase a similar recorder, made by Creed and Co., Telegraph Engineers of Croydon. The cost of the recorder is £26-7-6. A valve amplifier to supplement the ordinary wireless set will also be required, but the number of valves required (one to three) is partly a matter of experiment. The parts for this could be purchased, and the amplifier built by the staff. An estimate of cost is about £5 to £10." (No record of the outcome survives).

Efforts were made to cut down on meteorological expenditure. Special blocks were made so that the instrument charts could be printed locally. This resulted in a 75% saving on costs. Barograph charts were re-cycled after each leap year.

Meteorological services in the late 19th and late 20th centuries had much in common, although the relationship between health and weather was evidently considered to be more important in the early years - information was sent to the medical officers of health of most towns in the area. From then, until closure in 2004, the legal profession used Bidston's data - in fact one firm of solicitors was still a regular client after more than 130 years. Weather reports have been provided to solicitors throughout Bidston's history. For instance a report was issued following a collision in the Mersey between the

School Ship Conway and No 13 hopper on 3rd August 1900. From time to time meteorological staff have been required to attend court as expert witnesses.

The means of acquiring a certified weather report was quite complicated in the early years. First, a letter had to be sent to the solicitor of the Mersey Docks and Harbour Board, parent body to the Observatory, requesting permission to extract data. Then a clerk of the firm was allowed on to the premises to extract the data in person. The report was verified by the signature of the Director or his deputy. However, no charge was made for this service. At Bidston in the 1990s we were happy to provide statistics to anyone who requested them, but the service was free of charge only to schools or students.

Notes from Bidston Annual Reports
"For many years prior to 1936 Bidston was fully engaged in obtaining and transmitting several times a day observations which were used, along with others, in the forecasting service of the Meteorological Office. It was during these years that the scientific staff at the Observatory became popularly associated with the weather, and the daily reports and forecasts were much appreciated locally.

When the amalgamation (between the University's Tidal Institute and the Observatory) took place on Jan 1st 1929 it was fully intended that the meteorological and seismic activities of the Observatory should be maintained and developed, but shortly afterwards the Meteorological Office decided to make increased use of the observations taken at their own stations in the British Isles and so discontinued the use of observations from external stations. This meant that financial assistance from the Government was stopped. The amount of labour which could be used for meteorological observing had to be restricted in an increasing degree, and so time could not usually be spared for indulgence in meteorological forecasting. This explanation is necessary to explain why Bidston forecasts are not now made for the local enthusiasts, except on special occasions."

Sample of Weather Information supplied daily to the Press: dated June 1928

Bidston, Wednesday Night,- Following a rather warm night, ideal summer conditions have prevailed today, with a cloudless sky, brilliant sunshine, and light breezes, which prevented the heat from becoming unduly oppressive. The temperature rose from 64 degrees at 7 a.m. to a maximum of 73.2 degrees this afternoon, this being the fifth occasion this year on which 70 degrees or over has been recorded, the last occasion being on May 30th. The mean temperature is now 5.5 degrees above the average. This is the first instance since June 13th on which the mean has exceeded the normal. Winds have been from between west and south-west, varying little in direction all day, and being considerably lighter in force. The barometer rose very slightly until noon, and since then, in spite of small oscillations, has been on the whole steady. With very little cloud and practically no haze, very good visibility has been recorded, the Great Orme Head being easily distinguishable. Humidity has been on the whole moderate, though rather higher than yesterday's value.

For previous 24 hours:-

Maximum thermometer	73.9 F. (Fahrenheit)
Minimum thermometer	59.5 F.
Grass minimum thermometer	53.9 F.
Rainfall	Nil
Sunshine	14.3 hours.

9 p.m. reading

Barometer	30.20 inches rising
Dry bulb thermometer	64.0 F.
Wet bulb thermometer	58.5 F.
Humidity	71 per cent
Wind direction	SW

A letter to Mr. Roberts, Secretary of LOTI Committee, dated December 19th 1935, reads:-

"Dear Roberts,

Doodson and I have been giving further consideration to the question of the meteorological observations which are taken late each evening at the Observatory.

We consider that the number and efficiency of our automatic instruments have now reached a stage at which their readings may be taken to replace personal observation at one of the standard hours of the day. Such an arrangement would lead to an increase in the total amount of work done by Bigelstone and Corkan, as their time would not be so cut up as it is at present.

On adopting such a plan we could manage with a girl in Kirkland's place, if, on two evenings in the week, the girls were required to stay until 6 p.m.

Will you please put this suggestion before Mr. Beazley and Mr. Warner and ask whether they approve of such an arrangement?
Yours sincerely,
J. Proudman

PS   What the Committee decided, I think, was that it is undesirable for the girls to stay until 9 p.m., rather than that it is undesirable ever to extend their hours beyond 4.30 p.m. as your minute suggests."
(The situation arose because George Kirkland was planning to take up an appointment with the Air Ministry, possibly in meteorology.)

Reply dated Dec 30th 1935 (N.B. No long Christmas breaks in those days!):-

"Dear Professor Proudman,
In reply to your letter of the 19th Instant with regard to the staff at the Observatory, I have now had an opportunity of consulting with Colonel Beazley, Mr. Warner and also Sir Richard D. Holt, who have authorized me to say that they will have no objection to the Lady Computers at the Observatory being kept on duty until 6 p.m. on two evenings in the week and also to the appointment of a Lady Assistant in Kirkland's place.
In these circumstances no doubt you will proceed as you consider necessary."

Weather reports were sent to the Meteorological Office at 7 a.m, 1 p.m and 6 p.m daily, the evening 9 p.m one now being discontinued.

The Doodson family owned a spaniel 'Twee' who was rather fond of picking the grass minimum thermometer off the ground - fortunately he had a soft mouth.

The photo shows nine members of the Bidston 'Met' team photographed about 1980. They are: (left to right) Joyce Richards, Joyce Scoffield, Barbara Duff, Neil Hanson, Sylvia Asquith (leader), Sheila Shaw, Graham Williams, Libby McLeod and Rose Player.

Some notes on aspects of the weather:-

Temperature

On January 25th 1881 Bidston recorded a minimum air temperature of 8.5 F (-13.1 C). toward the end of a 21 day period during which the mean daily temperature did not rise above freezing point. The Observatory archive has a letter of confirmation in John Hartnup's handwriting, dated 1884. In 2004 this record still stood.

On August 1st 1990 we registered our highest-ever air temperature 94.5 F (34.7 C.), the first time on record that the temperature at Bidston has exceeded 90 F. Hill fires broke out close to the Observatory that afternoon, rendering a very hot day even more unbearable.

Rainfall

Frontal systems often approach from the SW, and, as Bidston lies to an extent in the shelter of the Welsh hills, rainfall totals are not generally high, but heavy falls can occur in showers. For instance, nearly ¾ inch fell in one hour on 24th July 1872. This contributed to a total of 1160 mm of rain for the whole year 1872, the wettest year on record to date. Summer and autumn saw the bulk of this rainfall. In only one other year, 2000, has the rainfall totalled more than 1000 mm. On one notable occasion, September 19th 1875, a thunderstorm caused severe flooding in Heswall, about four miles SW of Bidston. The deputy organist, John Heveran, a schoolmaster from Neston, and the bellows boy, Henry Rathbone, a farm servant, were both killed during evening service. The coroner, Henry Churton (presumably the same Henry Churton who would preside at the inquest on John Hartnup in 1892 - See Chapter Six), found the cause of death was lightning travelling down the weathervane and passing down the flagpole into the church. Many other buildings in the area were damaged, and a horse, pulling a tram along Hoylake Road, was also a victim.[6] A cloudburst on June 20th 1932, when almost an inch of rain fell in less than an hour, caused widespread flooding and damage in Liverpool and district. Many of us remember the drought of August 1976 (only 2.6 mm), but it is interesting to note that the following month, September, was the wettest on record of all months of the year (204.3 mm). More than half of this rainfall fell during the period 21st-26th September. So, while the summer of 1976 was the driest on record at Bidston, the autumn was the second wettest after 1872.

Due to Bidston's close proximity to the sea, snowfall tends to be lighter and less frequent than at inland sites, whilst air and ground frost occur less often than in surrounding low-lying areas. However the fringes of the Rivers Mersey and Dee have been known to freeze over in very cold conditions.

On a personal note, I particularly remember the harsh winter of 1962-63 when the ground was under snow for several weeks. One morning I alighted from the bus at the top of Ford Hill, meeting up with Moira Naylor, a colleague at Bidston, and we headed along Vyner Road and up on to the hill past the windmill. Walking across the hill to the Observatory was our normal route to work in those days - there was no thought of danger. It had snowed heavily overnight, and it took us a lot longer than usual to trudge through the snow. We were quite pleased with ourselves when we finally arrived, and somewhat disgruntled to be called to the Director's room, and be told off for being late!

Wind

The prevailing wind at the Observatory varies between W and NW, and gales are almost invariably from this direction. On February 10th 1928 Bidston recorded its highest gust, 104 mph (90 knots).

Sunshine

In Bidston's long sunshine record, dating from 1908, two years are outstanding: -

In 1911 we recorded 1766 hours of sunshine, of which 1006 hours occurred during the months May-August. The only other year where the summer hours exceeded 1000 was 1989, when the figure was 1025 hours and the total for the year was 1776 hours.

Visibility

In 1957 Mr. Reynolds, a keen meteorologist on the Observatory staff since 1951, studied two years of visibility observations, comparing views over the industrial areas of Liverpool and Birkenhead with those obtained by looking toward Wales. Industrial smoke caused a 25% reduction of visibility in the mornings and 10% in the afternoons. Domestic fire effect was estimated to account for a 25% to 40% decrease in visibility.

Westerly winds were found to be accompanied by visibility 3 to 7 times better than winds with easterly components. An article on the survey was contributed to "Weather" magazine.

Barometric Pressure

The lowest and highest values of barometric pressure at Bidston were both recorded in the nineteenth century - 939.7 millibars (27.75 inches) on 8th December 1886 and 1050.5 millibars (31.02 inches) on 9th January 1896.

An observer reads the thermometers in the Stevenson screen.

The above photograph was taken in 1992 when the new automated Bidston weather station was under test.

Under the new system signals from the automatic sensors (measuring temperature and relative humidity) were being transmitted by cable to digital monitors located inside the Observatory.

Under the old system (used since before 1845) the two upright thermometers measured dry bulb and wet bulb temperatures. The wet bulb temperature was achieved by wrapping the bulb of the thermometer in a small circle of muslin, kept moist by water rising up a cotton wick. A slide rule was then used to manually calculate relative humidity from these two readings. The horizontal thermometers indicated maximum and minimum temperatures, and were re-set at 0900 GMT each day.

Chapter Nineteen

The "Zephyr"

In the mid 1930s, Dr. Doodson designed a current meter to measure the speed, direction and degree of turbulence of deep sea currents and in order to test this instrument at sea, the University of Liverpool purchased a small Manx herring drifter, the Zephyr, and converted it for scientific use. Between 1936 and 1939 several trips were made during the summer months to a research area six sea miles offshore from Port St. Mary, Isle of Man, to test the current meter and also to test Favé offshore tide gauges, which were a type of pressure gauge utilising a motor tyre inner tube. Three of these gauges were placed on the sea bed and all were successfully recovered.

The Zephyr

The Zephyr was crewed by Professor Proudman, Dr. Doodson, Dr. R. J. Daniel of Liverpool University Oceanographic Department, who was Director of the University Biological Station at Port Erin, Mr. Bigelstone and two students. Harry Corkan, himself a native of the Isle of Man, later took the place of Mr Bigelstone. The Zephyr's skipper was Captain Edward (Ned) Maddrell of Glenchass, Port St. Mary, and a Manx engineer, Mr. H. C. Cain, was also aboard. Ned's son, Ed, often sailed out on the Zephyr as cabin boy. Ed recalled how the boat had a steam-operated winch, and only a small cabin to provide shelter from the weather. The trips lasted for periods of 12 hours, and engine failure was not unknown. Ned was paid £45 for three months of the year to look after the Zephyr. At weekends during the rest of the year he checked the drifter at its moorings, but received no extra payment.

According to an Isle of Man press cutting, the tests were being operated from three points, each six miles offshore from Port St. Mary, and the total exercise was to last six weeks.[1]

On one occasion the current meter was lost when the hawser attached to it gave way under stormy conditions. Eventually the search had to be called off as night fell and the weather further deteriorated. Ed recalled how Professor Proudman stood on deck and used semaphore to signal to another vessel, which had offered assistance, to call off the search. In an interview with a local Isle of Man newspaper, Professor Proudman reported that the instrument had cost £100 to build and was the only one in existence. It represented years of investigation and its loss "had hampered their work to a considerable degree." For two days bad weather prevented the search, and there is no record of whether they ever found the current meter.

The tests were brought to a stop by the outbreak of war and the Zephyr was sold. It is rumoured that after the war vandals boarded the Zephyr and set fire to her. She consequently sank. However, after the war, Professor Proudman persuaded the University to purchase a bigger and better vessel for the joint use of the Oceanography Department in conjunction with Bidston and the Marine Biological Station at Port Erin. Further experiments were made, based on earlier experience gained from the Zephyr trips, and numerous scientific papers were written as a result.

This was to prove the start of an ongoing series of research cruises which would cover an ever-widening area of the oceans, and utilise purpose-built research ships up to and beyond the turn of the century.

Chapter Twenty

Regulations for the Testing of Marine Chronometers - 1907

Office (at Observatory) open: 10 a.m. to 2 p.m. each weekday.

Every chronometer must be left for testing for not less than six weeks, and must then be removed within one month after notice, otherwise a charge of one shilling per week is made.

Any temperature between 45°F. and 95° F.

Any instrument can be returned for testing at any time in the next 12 months free of charge.

Charges
Chronometers - (2 day or 8 day) - 10/-.
Watches

Class	Period of testing	Charge
A	48 days -7 periods of 6 days (not Sundays)	21/-
B	34 days -5 periods of 6 days (not Sundays)	10/6d
C	20 days -3 periods of 6 days (not Sundays)	5/6d

Class A

Period - Position of watch		Temperature
1	Horizontal, dial up	50°F
2	Horizontal, dial up	65°F
3	Horizontal, dial up	80°F
4	Pendant up	60°F

5	Vertical, but turned through 90°angle	60°F
6	As above, but hour 3 brought to top	60°F
7	Dial downwards	60°F

Class B

Period	- Position of watch	Temperature
1	Vertical	50°F
2	Vertical	65°F
3	Vertical	80°F
4	Horizontal, dial up	60°F
5	Horizontal, dial down	60°F

Class C

Period	- Position of watch	Temperature
1	Horizontal, dial up	Constant
2	Horizontal, dial down	Constant
3	Vertical, pendant up	Constant

Class A

Certificate granted if:-

1. Daily rate not more than two seconds from the mean rate for the same period.
2. The mean daily rate remains less than 10 seconds at any stage of the test.
3. A change of 10°F. does not affect mean daily rate more than 3 seconds.
4. Change in mean daily rate from its normal or first position in any two consecutive periods does not exceed 5 seconds.

Class B

1. As 1 above, but four seconds.

2. As 2 above, but fifteen seconds.
3. As 3 above, but five seconds.
4. As 4 above, but ten seconds.

Class C: - Two conditions
As B2 but that the difference in rate between any two consecutive days does not exceed six seconds.

Charges for other instruments
Superior sextants -	6/-
Common sextants -	3/6d
Compasses -	2/6d
Theodolites -	7/6d
Marine telescopes and superior binoculars -	2/9d
Pocket telescopes and opera glasses -	2/6d
Barometers and aneroids -	5/- to 10/6d
Thermometers -	1/- to 5/-
Raingauges -	2 /6d
Glass Measures -	1/-
Small Robinson Cup Anemometers with dials directly compared with Standard -	7/6d

By 1928 the charges had increased to:-
Superior sextants -	9/-
Common sextants -	5/-

Chapter Twenty - one

Four Examples of Expertise

1. Earth Tides

In 1966 a long term research programme into earth tides was started at Bidston by Dr. Rossiter, Geoffrey Lennon and Norman Heaps.

The movements in the solid earth below the sea bed have a small effect on ocean tides. In the deep cellars at Bidston there were two gravity meters recording movements of the earth and the readings were being compared with those from a gravity meter installed down a mineshaft at Llanryst in North Wales. The deep cellars at Bidston, recording the exceptionally large loading and attractive effects of the nearby Irish Sea, were an ideal site. The information from gravity meters was used to increase knowledge of the elasticity of the earth as a whole, the effects on the earth's core, and details of the structure of the crust and upper mantle.

Trevor Baker, Dr. Vanicek and Graham Jeffries joined Geoffrey Lennon in 1969, thus freeing Dr. Rossiter and Norman Heaps to concentrate on other research. A Lacoste and Romberg Gravitymeter continued to give readings in the vaults at Bidston, while the Llanrwst underground station was used to test a Vertical Pendulum (to measure the earth's tilt) on loan from Clausthal in West Germany.

In 1970 the Bidston station was out of action for much of the year due to renovations being made on site, but the time was devoted to research work on Horizontal Pendulums.

As a result of the successful tests with the Claustral pendulum, Bidston acquired a Graf-Askania vertical pendulum of its own, and installed it after modification.
A comparison of data records showed that Bidston was susceptible to diurnal and seasonal variation in temperature and air pressure, but Llanrwst was free from this.

In March 1972 a tidal gravity meter, specifically designed for ICOT was delivered and installed at Bidston, and in 1974 a prototype one metre base length tilt meter, developed at the University of Manchester Institute of Science and Technology (UMIST), was tested for three months in the Bidston vault, prior to installation at the Royal Greenwich Observatory at Herstmonceaux, where the effects of earth tidal movements on the PZT (Photographic Zenith Tube) telescope were to be assessed.

In 1976 it was decided to start a new tilt measurement program at Bassenthwaite in the Lake District. Two 30 metre deep boreholes and one 12 metre deep hole, each 30 centimetres in diameter, were drilled. It was found that rises in water level, following periods of heavy rain, caused a measurable tilt variation.

Members of staff from Bidston installed a tidal gravity meter in the Valle de Los Caidos, near Madrid, for the period February to November 1979. This was a joint experiment with the University of Madrid to measure the effect of the relatively large North Atlantic ocean tide on the Iberian Peninsula.

Over the years the Bidston staff was involved in experiments carried out in conjunction with many International Centres such as Frankfurt, Brussels and Zurich.
The resulting readings were of particular significance for attempts in various parts of the world to use long period tilt and strain measurements for earthquake prediction.

2. Tide Gauge Inspectorate

In 1970 the Institute assumed responsibility for servicing the National Working party on Tide Gauges for the Land Drainage Division of MAFF (Ministry of Agriculture, Fisheries and Food). Geoffrey Lennon was appointed Chairman.

Dr. Pugh was extensively testing Neyrpic bubbler gauges at Birkenhead and Hilbre Island. These pneumatic gauges were easier and cheaper to produce than conventional stilling well gauges, and proved to be accurate to 2 cm even on coasts exposed to wave action. Plans were made for these to be installed on oilrigs or Trinity House towers.
Douglas Leighton, a staff member who had originally supervised the "computers" operating the tide prediction machines, was appointed as Tide Gauge Inspector. His remit was to develop a system of quality control by regular visits

to tide gauges. He travelled the country visiting the sites in the 'A' class Tide Gauge network, and helping with advice on six new stations.

By 1975 the number of gauges around the coast of the U.K. had risen to 34, and the Tide Gauge Inspectorate was doubled. Douglas Leighton having moved to the Marine Operations Section, two staff members, Bill Ainscow and Alan Browell, were appointed to operate the service. They were responsible for visiting the sites around the country and carrying out any necessary repairs or modifications, thus ensuring that the tide gauges were working to the best of their capacity and good annotated records were being produced. The Inspectors gave advice and assistance, and on-site training as required, in order to solve problems and improve standards. The sites ranged from the Shetland Isles to the Channel Isles, so Bill and Alan were involved in a great deal of travel.

Advice was also given on choice of tide gauges to outside bodies such as Regional Water Authorities.

Further tide gauge installations in late 1977 were made in Iceland, in Eire, on a gas platform and at the Inner Dowsing light tower. Timing records were improved by quartz crystal clock units which eliminated the need for time corrections.

In 1977 arrangements were made with the Meteorological Office for a datalink between Bidston and Bracknell in order to carry out real time sea level forecasting tests at Bidston. This was delayed until early 1978.

In 1983 the Dataring communication system was introduced so that tide gauge information could be recorded remotely. This would eventually consist of 36 permanent shore-based tide gauges and a centralized monitoring data collection system. The sites at Ifracombe and Newlyn (Cornwall) were the first to be updated. The data from them was transmitted via a midnight line facility on the public switched telephone network.

By 1984 Dataring had been installed at Avonmouth, Holyhead and North Shields. The Central Dataring station at Bidston was operational from the beginning of that year.

There were 13 stations on Dataring by January 1988. The STWS (Storm Tide Warning Service) at Bracknell started monitoring tidal signals from ten remote sites along the east and Channel coasts using a new system called Dataflow designed at POL, Bidston.

By 1990 Dataring had grown to 27 stations, and the following year the Dataflow system was providing real time data to the STWS and to the Thames Barrier operations room.

Dave Smith and Les Bradley took over as Tide Gauge Inspectors in 1991 following the retirement of Bill Ainscow and Alan Browell.

By 1993 Dataflow output was being sent to RIKS, the National Institute for Coastal and Marine Management in Holland, where the risk of flooding from storm surges was even greater than in the U.K.

NTSLF (the National Tide and Sea Level Facility) was set up in 2002. The UK National Tide Gauge Network now comprises 45 sites. NTSLF is responsible for these, together with the seven sites set up by members of Bidston staff in Antarctica and the South Atlantic. Dave Smith and Les

Bradley continue as Tide Gauge Inspectors, and the Facility is funded by DEFRA (the Department for Environment, Food and Rural Affairs).
Most recently an innovative radar tide gauge has been installed in Gibraltar.

3. PSMSL

The PSMSL (Permanent Service for Mean Sea Level) was first set up by Professor Proudman in 1933 to collect and analyse sea level data from tide gauges around the British coast. As time went on data was collected from overseas, but financial and staff limitation meant that sea level investigation was limited. In the late 1960s the PSMSL was formally set up. The group was headed by Mr. Lennon, assisted by Dr. Pugh. Dr. Rossiter was appointed as its Director.

Data was now being collected from sites worldwide, and datum problems generated frequent correspondence. Much of this work was carried out by Carol Jones.

Following the loss of its Director, Dr. Rossiter, in 1972, PSMSL lost another key worker when Carol Jones married Dr. David Pugh and resigned her post. Geoffrey Lennon was invited to take over the Directorship of PSMSL, and a new recruit, Elaine Barrow, took over from Carol as Technical Secretary.

Work was started on a publication of monthly and annual means of sea level values for sites worldwide:
Volume 1 would cover Europe, Africa, India and the Far East

and, if grants were available, Volume 2 would cover America and Volume 3 would cover the rest of the world. Volume 1, bringing to fruition much of Dr. Rossiter's work, was distributed worldwide in 1977.

When Geoffrey Lennon moved to Australia in 1978, he retained the Directorship of PSMSL, and Dr. David Pugh became Honorary Director of the Service.

In the mid 1980s an IOC (Intergovernmental Oceanographic Commission) task team of interested scientists led by Dr. David Pugh and Professor Klaus Wyrtki of the University of Hawaii set up GLOSS (Global Sea Level Observing System).
One object of GLOSS was to set up courses for overseas tide gauge operators, each course lasting two to three weeks. The first courses were held at Bidston from 1983 - 1990 inclusive. The courses were attended by operators from South America and Africa. Lectures were given by experts on the Bidston staff, including the Tide Gauge Inspectorate, Dr. Pugh and Graham Alcock, who was a specialist in deep sea tide gauges. Thereafter other countries took turns in hosting these events.

Following a move by Dr. Pugh to NERC headquarters, Dr. Philip Woodworth (later Professor Woodworth) took charge of PSMSL, and continues in that post. In 2003 he was awarded a Certificate of Appreciation for service to IOC and for chairing the GLOSS program.
Elaine Barrow married Bob Spencer, a key Bidston instrument engineer, and they both took early retirement in 1999. Elaine was awarded an MBE for her services to the PSMSL over

25 years. Rose Player took over from Elaine as Technical Support Secretary to the PSMSL.

Financial support for the PSMSL was and is provided by the Federation of Astronomical and Geophysical Services (FAGS) by the Intergovernmental Oceanographic Commission and by NERC.

4. The British Oceanographic Data Centre

The year 1976 saw the setting up of NERC MIAS (the NERC Marine Information and Advisory Service) at the behest of the Department of Industry and Energy, which requested a major increase in resources to supply marine information and data to all who could make use of them. The service would consist of a number of full time staff, initially based at IOS (Institute of Oceanographic Sciences) Wormley. This service replaced and expanded the former BODS (British Oceanographic Data Service), set up in 1969. The purpose of MIAS was to set up a data bank of information on waves, currents and tide gauge readings. The data bank would be installed on the new computer (Honeywell 66/20) due to be installed at Bidston, and an enquiry office would be opened to deal with customers. MIAS was greatly expanded the following year, and now involved a tenth of the entire IOS staff, headed by Mr. Brian Hinde.

In early 1977 MIAS was formally launched as the U.K. National Oceanographic Data Centre and was confirmed by the Intergovernmental Oceanographic Commission as the body responsible internationally for wave data from all over the world. A Tidal Advisory Service was set up at Bidston.

The years 1982 -1983 saw a rapid growth in data acquired from oceanic, geophysical and bathymetry sources, together with sea level data and remote sensed wave data. There was a sharp increase in the use of the data especially by researchers. Most interest was shown in wave data - over one third of all enquiries.

From 1980 to 1989 Dr. Meirion Jones led the Bidston section of MIAS. In April 1989 MIAS was renamed BODC (British Oceanographic Data Centre). It was now sited wholely at Bidston, and from 1989 until his retirement in 2002 Dr. Jones continued in charge.

The large amount of data acquired was used by BODC to publish the UK Marine Digital Atlas and the General Bathymetric Chart of the Oceans.

BODC is now the United Kingdom's National Oceanographic Data Centre and acts on behalf of NERC as the Designated Data Centre for Marine Data. It also has a special role as the Data Centre for the United Kingdom National Tide Gauge Network. By 2003 the number of staff had risen to 31, and was headed by Dr. Juan Brown.

REFERENCES

Introduction

1   "Pictorial Relics of Ancient Liverpool" -
W.G.Herdman - Liverpool Record Office,
Central Library, Liverpool.

Chapter One - The Flag System

1   Extracts from the Minutes of the Common Council
of the Borough of Liverpool 1679 -1772: MDHB/
MP/1/25 - MDHB Archive - Merseyside Maritime Museum.

2   Engraving showing the flags on Bidston Hill - H. F. James - Courtesy
Williamson Art Gallery.

3   The Vyner Papers - Cheshire Record Office, Chester.

4   Memorials of Liverpool - Volume 1 - J A Picton FSA
1875

5   "History of Liverpool" - J. Wallace - 1795 - Section 2
(Also attributed to Dr. W. Moss 1801).

6   Display in Merseyside Maritime Museum.

7   'Signalling Ships at Liverpool 80 years ago' -
George Wilson - Palatine Notebook - 1883 - Volume
3, Page 91 - Liverpool Record Office, Central
Library, Liverpool.

8   'The Struggles and Adventures of Christopher
Tadpole at Home and Abroad' - Albert Smith -
Published 1847- 48.

9   As 5.

10   Ibid.

11   A map of the County Palatine of Chester - Wirral
Museum Archive.

12   DBC 4710 Box 18 F2 - Cheshire Record Office,
Chester.

Chapter Two - Bidston Lighthouse

1   The Internet

2   Memorials of Liverpool - Volume 1 - J A Picton FSA
- 1875.

3   Liverpool Town Books - page 777 - Liverpool
Record Office, Central Library, Liverpool.

4   "House of Commons Journal" - Volume 9 - Internet

5   Captain H.M.Denham, R.N. - 1840.

6   Birkenhead Central Reference Library.

7   Extracts from the Minutes of the Common Council
of the Borough of Liverpool 1679 - 1772. MDHB/
MP/1/25 - MDHB Archive at Merseyside Maritime
Museum.

8   A New Chart of the West Coast of England from
Point Lynas, Anglesey to Formby Point - 1783 -
Williamson Art Gallery, Birkenhead.

9   "The Voyages & Cruises of Commodore Walker" - H. S. Vaughan

10   Courtesy the Science Museum.

11   "Liverpool's Part in the Lighthouse Revolution
- The truth that saved thousands of lives" - Colin
Fryer: The Liverpool Star - 6th March 1986.

12   "Sailing Instructions from Point Lynas to
Liverpool" - Captain H.M.Denham, R.N. - 1840.
Liverpool Record Office, Central Library, Liverpool.

13   As 7.

14   Ibid.

15   Ref. YPX/90/20 - Wirral Museum Archive.

16   "An Inquiry into the Position of the Alleged Old
Lighthouses of Wallasey/Leasowe and the Ancient
Village of Altmouth" - Joseph Boult - Liverpool
Courier - October 22nd 1856.

17   As 7.

18   Ibid.

19   As 2 and as 10.

20   "John Phillips and the Small Lighthouses" -
E.C.Woods - HSCL Volume 100 - 1948.

21   "Twixt Mersey and Dee" - Hilda Gamlin -1897.

22   "English Lighthouse Tours, 1801, 1813 and 1818"
from the diaries of Robert Stevenson, edited by
Alan Stevenson - 1946.

23   "The World's Lighthouses before 1820" - D. Alan
Stevenson.

24   "History of the Hundred of Wirral" - William
Mortimer - 1847.

25	MDHB/MP/4 - Sub-Committee for the Department of the Marine Surveyor 1847- 1857 Volume 1 - MDHB Archive at Merseyside Maritime Museum.
26	Ibid.
27	Ibid.
28	MDHB/MP/13 Volume 1 - Report of the Inspection of Telegraphs, Lighthouses, Lightships, etc. - MDHB Archive at Merseyside Maritime Museum.
29	Ordnance Survey Maps for 1872 and 1909 - Birkenhead Central Reference Library.
30	MDHB Legal Document - 1935 - MDHB Archive at Merseyside Maritime Museum.

Chapter Three - Semaphore Station

1	'The Semaphore' - T.W.Holmes - 1983.
2	'Memorials of Liverpool' - Volume 1 - J A Picton FSA - 1875.
3	The Internet.
4	Memorials of Liverpool - Volume 2 - J A Picton FSA - 1875.
5	'The Old Telegraphs' - B.G. Wilson - 1976.
6	As 4.
7	Details from 'Marine Art and Liverpool, Paintings,Places and Flag Codes 1760 -1960' - A.S.Davidson .
8	As 5.
9	As 1.
10	Liverpool Mercury - April 13th 1827.
11	Details from 'A Telegraphic Vocabulary adapted for the Line of Semaphoric Telegraphs from Liverpool to Holyhead' - Lieutenant William Lord R.N. - 1845.
12	As 7.
13	Codes and ship names from 11 and 14.
14	"Numerical List of Vessels for the Holyhead - Liverpool Signal Station" - J. Outram circa 1828 - Liverpool Record Office, Central Library, Liverpool.
15	As 5.

16   Liverpool Mercury - October 26th 1827.
17   Liverpool Mercury - November 2nd 1827.
18   Liverpool Mercury - November 6th 1827
19   Dock Sub-Committee Minutes - MDHB Archive at
       Merseyside Maritime Museum.
20   Broadsheet on display in Merseyside Maritime
       Museum.
21   As 11.
22   MDHB/MP/4 Volume 1- Marine Surveyor's
       and Water Bailiff's Letter Books - MDHB Archive
       at Merseyside Maritime Museum.
23   Ibid
24   MDHB/MP/4 Volume 2 - Marine Surveyor's
       and Water Bailiff's Letter Books - MDHB Archive
       at Merseyside Maritime Museum.
25   As 5.
26   As 22.

Chapter Four - Waterloo Dock Observatory : Bidston's Precursor
1   'The Rise and Progress of Liverpool 1551-1835 - J.
       Touzeau - 1910; also 'Transactions of the Historic
       Society of Lancashire and Cheshire' (HSLC) -
       Volume 22: 1869 - 70.
2   'An Essay towards the History of Liverpool' -
       Enfield - 1773
3   "The Development and Work of the Liverpool
       Observatory at Waterloo Dock 1836 - 1866" - Paul
       Dearden - a Dissertation submitted for an MSc. in
       the History of Science and Technology - A 270/2/6
       - Sydney Jones Library - University of Liverpool.
4   'Liverpool Central Docks 1799-1905' - Adrian
       Jarvis - 1991.
5   Observatory Committee Minute Book: 1836-1856
       - Liverpool Record Office, Central Library,
       Liverpool.
6   "Northwest Astronomers - William Lassell" - Gerard
       Gilligan - 1994.
7   As 5.
8   Ibid.
9   "Sailing Instructions from Point Lynas to

Liverpool" - Captain H.M.Denham, R.N. - 1840
- Liverpool Record Office, Central Library,
Liverpool.

10	As 5.
11	Dock Committee Minute Book: 1836-1856 - Liverpool Record Office, Central Library, Liverpool.
12	As 5.
13	Taylor and Sheepshank - Correspondence in the Liverpool Times and the Mercury 1845.
14	As 5.
15	As 4.
16	John Hartnup gave a detailed description (retrospectively) in his Annual Report to the Observatory Committee in 1883.
17	Annual reports of the Astronomer to the Observatory Committee 1849 - 1856.
18	Ibid.
19	Report of the Council to the 31st AGM of the Royal Astronomical Society 1850.
20	"The Marine Chronometer - Its History and Development" - Lieutenant Commander Rupert Gould.
21	Report of the Council to the AGM of the Royal Astronomical Society 1852.
22	"An account of the earliest successful experiments made in England in producing, by their own light, photographs of the moon and other heavenly bodies" - J.A.Forrest HSLC Volume 15 1862-63.
23	MDHB/MP13 volume 1 - MDHB Archive at Merseyside Maritime Museum.

Unless otherwise indicated the information in subsequent chapters of the book has been obtained from one of four sources:

a.	Documents in the library of Proudman Oceanographic Laboratory.
b.	Documents in the Archive of the World Museum, Liverpool.
c.	Proudman Oceanographic Laboratory Annual Reports 1970 - 2005.

d. Memories and memorabilia of present and
    former staff of Bidston Observatory (now Proudman
    Oceanographic Laboratory) and their relatives.

Chapter Five - Bidston:The Hartnup Era

1 Memorials of Liverpool - Volume 1 - J A Picton FSA
   - 1875.
2 The Internet
3 MDHB/MP13 Volume 1 – Minutes of Marine
   Committee - MDHB Archive at Merseyside
   Maritime Museum.
4 "John Hartnup - A Biography" by Henry F. Watt,
   Vice-President of the MMSA (Mercantile Marine
   Service Association) Published in "MMSA
   Reporter" - January 1886.
5 Ibid.

Chapter Six - Bidston - John Hartnup Junior: Director 1885 - 1892

1 Birkenhead News - April 23rd 1892
2 Birkenhead News - April 30th 1892.

Chapter Seven - Life at Bidston in the Late 19th Century

1 Letter from Professor Herschel to George Higgs
   15th May 1892.
2 "Oliver Lodge and the Liverpool Physical Society"
   - Peter Rowlands - 1990.
3 Survey of Bidston Lighthouse and Observatory (for drainage)" - 1848
   - Wirral Museum Archive.
4 "British Association Excursion Guide Book" - First
   Edition - 1896 - Liverpool Record Office, Central
   Library, Liverpool.

Chapter Eight -The Early Twentieth Century.

1 Liverpool Daily Post - 19th November 1902.
2 Liverpool Mercury - 21st November 1902.

3   The Daily Courier - 15th April 1875.
4   The Vyner Papers - Cheshire Record Office, Cheshire.

Chapter Nine - Bidston: The Inter-war Period

1   "The Rise of the Port of Liverpool" - C. Northcote
         Parkinson - 1952.
2   Extracts from the Minutes of the Common Council
         of the Borough of Liverpool 1679 - 1772. MDHB/
         MP/1/25 - MDHB Archive - Merseyside Maritime
         Museum.
3   Tidal Institute Finance Records - (S 2147-48) -
         Special Scripts Archive - Sidney Jones Library -
         University of Liverpool.
4   Special Scripts Archive - Sidney Jones Library -
         University of Liverpool.

Chapter Ten - World War II

1   Press Report 29th June 1939.

Chapter Eleven - Bidston Observatory: Postwar

1   "Some Reminiscences" by Professor Proudman in
         the University of Liverpool   Recorder - Number 5
         -1954 - Tidal Institute Finance Records - (S 2147- 48) - Special
         Scripts Archive - Sidney Jones Library
         - University of Liverpool.

Chapter Twelve - The Rossiter Years

1   "Arthur Thomas Doodson -1890-1968" -
         "Biographical Memoirs of Fellows of the Royal
         Society" - Volume 14 - 1968 - Harold Cohen
         Library - University of Liverpool.
2   Liverpool Daily Post - March 19th - 1969.
3   Obituary - Daily Telegraph - May 1971.

Chapter Thirteen - The Bidston Story Continues

1   Information courtesy Professor G. W. Lennon.

Chapter Fourteen - Four Directors: Their Early Years

1   Report of the Council to the 66th AGM of the Royal
      Astronomical Society February 1886.
2   "Who was Who: 1916-28" - Harold Cohen Library
      - University of Liverpool.
3   "Obituary - W.E.Plummer" - Report of the Council
      to the 109th AGM of the Royal Astronomical
      Society.
4   Archive of Special Scripts Department - Sidney
      Jones Library - University of Liverpool.
5   Tribute from D.E.Cartwright and F.Ursell in
      "Biographical Memoirs of Fellows of the Royal
      Society" - Volume 22 1976 - Harold Cohen Library
      - University of Liverpool.
6   Collection of letters from Arthur Doodson
      to Margaret Gallagher 1914 -1918 - World Museum,
      Liverpool.

Chapter Fifteen - The One O'Clock Gun

1   MDHB/MP13 volume 1 - MDHB Archive -
      Merseyside Maritime Museum.
2   Archive of Special Scripts Department - Sydney
      Jones Library - University of Liverpool.

Chapter Sixteen - Astronomy

1   Monthly Notices of the Royal Astronomical Society
      - Volume 8 - November 1847 to June 1848.
2   Report of the Council to the 31st AGM of the Royal
      Astronomical Society 1852.
3   "Report on the Liverpool Equatorial" - Keith
      Hindley FRAS - early 1960s.

Chapter Eighteen - Meteorology

1   Gore's Directory of Liverpool 1829.
2   "West Kirby and Hilbre" - John Brownbill - 1928.
3   Ibid.

4   MDHB/MP/4 (as semaphore 22)
5   Report of the Council to the AGM of the Royal
        Astronomical Society 1852.
6   "St. Peters Church and Parish, Heswall" - a short history and guide
        - Rev. Canon Kenneth Lee

Chapter Nineteen – The "Zephyr"

1   The Examiner.

Further Sources Consulted

'Liverpool 1775-1800' - R.Brooke - 1853.
'Ancient Meols' - Rev. A. Hume - 1863.
'Auld Lang Syne' - Harry Neilson.
'The Hundred of Wirral' - Philip Sulley
'Hoylake and Meols Past' - Stephen J. Roberts 1992.
'Faster than the Wind' - Frank Large.